Identification & Price Guide

by Linda Mullins

Published by Hobby House Press, Inc.
Grantsville, Maryland
www.hobbyhouse.com

Teddy Bear Books by Linda Mullins:

Teddy Bears Past & Present, Volume I (Fifth Printing)
The Teddy Bear Men (Second Printing)
Raikes Bear and Doll Story (Two Editions)
Teddy Bears Past & Present, Volume II
Teddy Bear & Friends Price Guide
A Tribute to Teddy Bear Artists
American Teddy Bear Encyclopedia
Creating Heirloom Teddy Bears
A Tribute to Teddy Bear Artists — (Series 2)

Teddy's Bears
American Artist Teddy Bears — Patterns and Tips
A Tribute to Teddy Bear Artists — (Series 3))
Creating Heirloom Teddy Bears Pattern Book (Series 2)
Linda Mullins' Teddy Bear & Friends Identification & Price Guide
The Ultimate Handbook for Making Teddy Bears
Teddy Bear Centennial Book
Steiff Identification and Price Guide
Creating Miniature Teddy Bears — (Series 2)

(All books published by Hobby House Press, Grantsville, Maryland)

Additional copies of this book may be purchased at $29.95 (plus postage and handling) from
Hobby House Press, Inc.
1 Corporate Drive, Grantsville, MD 21536
1-800-554-1447
www.hobbyhouse.com
or from your favorite bookstore or dealer.

Printed in the United States of America

ISBN: 0-87588-612-4

Table of Contents

Dedication

In memory of Margarete Steiff,
who will always be affectionately remembered
for her love of children and her invaluable
contribution to the teddy bear world.

Acknowledgements

I have many people to thank for helping me with the preparation of this book. My husband Wally is at the top of the list. With his understanding and encouragement during 14 years of writing 17 books, he has surpassed all qualifications for a number one husband.

I wish to acknowledge a special debt of gratitude to Falk Thomas (Marketing & Sales Director of Margarete Steiff GmbH), Paul H. Johnson (President and Chief Executive Officer of Steiff North America, Inc.), Barbara Sprenger (Senior Vice President of Marketing of Steiff North America, Inc.), and Jone C. Victoria (Director, Club/Internet Steiff North America, Inc.).

A thanks also goes out to the following Steiff experts, stores, collectors, appraisers, auction houses and museums for sharing their knowledge and priceless collections: Daniel Agnew (Christie's South Kensington), Dottie Ayers (The Calico Teddy), Barbara Baldwin (Old Friends Antiques), Ruth Baum, Karen Chesbro, Judy and Lee Day, Yasuhiro Gawase, Mimi Hiscox, Barbara Lauver (Harper General Store), Ho Phi Lee, Horst Poestegens (Auctioneer, Germany), Ian Pout (Teddy Bears of Witney), Puppenhausmuseum (Basil, Switzerland), Deborah and Donald Ratliff, Dayle Rushall, Emma Stephens, Theriaults, Judy Vinson, Patricia Volpe, Lisa Vought (Dreamland Toys), Donna West, Carolyn Wiggins, Susan Wiley .

Thanks to Ray Boileau for his invaluable contribution regarding "Buying and Selling Steiff Online".

My special friend Georgi Bohrod deserves a big thank you for all her assistance, guidance and support. Her true personal interest and professional suggestions were of great importance to me.

Thanks also to my patient and well advising editor, Sherry White, to Brenda Wiseman for her tireless creativity in designing this book, to Patricia J. Matthews for her professional computer services, my photographer Bill Ahrend, and finally to my publisher, Gary R. Ruddell, for believing in me and this book.

Guidelines for Buying and Selling

One of the most popular ways to buy and sell collectibles is via the Internet. In fact, I have devoted an entire section to the phenomenon we call "online." However, nothing can replace the hands-on experience of discovering the consummate bear or animal for your collection.

A show or convention gives you the chance to visit with dealers, storeowners, and appraisers all under one roof. Check out specialty magazines such as *Teddy Bear and Friends* or *Teddy Bear Review*

for advertisements and notices of these special events. You'll also find advertisements for special teddy bear shops and dealers in these publications. Other fun ways to shop for bargains are garage sales and flea-markets. Sometimes an estate sale of furniture and household items will reveal a well-hidden gem. Once in a while, you'll find a teddy bear or two in your local paper's classified ads. From time to time, the major auction houses have special bear and doll sales as well.

Right: Photograph of bear from the illustration below with original owner. *Courtesy Christie's.*

Above: Bears that portray the special appeal that only comes with generations of love will not command the price or be looked upon by the majority of collectors as a good financial investment as will bears in good condition. Bear (Top left). Circa 1910. 10in (25cm); white mohair; shoe-button eyes. CONDITION: Fair. PRICE: £437 (approximately $648). Bear (Center left). Circa 1910. 13in (33cm); dark brown mohair; shoe-button eyes. CONDITION: Fair. PRICE: £747, (approximately $1,109). Bear (Bottom left). Circa 1910. 11-1/2in (29cm); dark cinnamon mohair; shoe-button eyes. CONDITION: Very good. PRICE: £1,840 (approx. $2,732). Bear (Right). Circa 1910. 9-1/2in (24cm); white mohair; shoe-button eyes. CONDITION: Fair. PRICE: £483 (approximately $717). Bears sold at Christie's South Kensington December 6, 1999 auction. *Courtesy Christie's.*

Above: Bears with provenance or documentation of their origin can command high prices. Bear (Left). Circa 1908. 23in (58cm); blond mohair; shoe-button eyes; f.j.; e.s.; FF button. See top right illustration for picture of this bear with original owner. CONDITION: Fair. English Bear (Right). Circa 1950. 7-1/2in (19cm); cotton plush; glass eyes; f.j.; e.s. CONDITION: Fair. PRICE (two bears and photograph of original owner): £4,112 (approximately $6,106). Sold at Christie's South Kensington December 4, 2000. *Courtesy Christie's.*

Left: Rare and wonderful Steiff teddy bears and animals have passed through the old and renowned Christie's South Kensington Auction House in London. Steiff Bear. Circa 1912. 19-½in; black mohair; shoe-button eyes with red felt disc backing; f.j.; e.s.; <u>FF</u> button with remains of white S.L. CONDITION: Excellent. PRICE: £91,750, (approximately $136,248). Sold at Christie's South Kensington December 4, 2000 auction. *Courtesy Christie's.*

Right: Renowned British Steiff dealer Ian Pout, owner of Teddy Bears of Witney, in his shop with some of his Steiff bears.

Buying for Investment

Few people buy Steiff strictly as an investment. Mostly they buy Steiff because they like it. Assembling a Steiff collection can become quite costly with averages in the hundreds of dollars. However, even though there is no guarantee that any particular Steiff will appreciate consistently, the track record for old or antique Steiffs is good. Most collectors expect to at least break even if they eventually sell their Steiff.

There are many factors to consider when buying a Steiff. This section will outline some of them. The most important concept to remember is that if you are not an expert, always purchase from someone you trust. Other than confidence in yourself and/or the person from whom you are buying there are five factors to take into consideration:

1. Condition
2. Rarity
3. Identification Marks (i.e., Steiff button, stock label and chest tag)
4. Size
5. Special circumstances such as age, provenance, facial expression, color and/or mechanical performance.

As a general rule, the better the condition the higher the price. Bare spots, moth holes, patched paws and the like signify price reductions. However, there are those who favor

"played with" conditions which add to a certain intangible interest and value. Such items are very hard to price. Some collectors can tolerate worn, or slightly worn pads, but most require excellent fur covering. And then there is the demand for the pristine condition, "shop-new," of replicas and other collectible Steiffs produced since 1980.

So, it is important to note that the prices quoted here are GUIDELINES ONLY and adhere to general standards. You'll see one-time flukes at auction, which result in record prices, but these are the exception. The listed price gaps are an attempt to bridge regional price differences and to allow for negotiating based on the various components that constitute the worth of an item. Once more, the most important axiom, "When in doubt, consult an expert!"

Steiff teddy bears and animals that are most sought after often have the following characteristics:

- Unusual fur coloring and/or design
- Mechanical functions
- Produced for special occasions
- Produced in small numbers
- Musical movement
- Advertising or promotional purposes
- Steiff ear button (adds 10-25% in value)
- Original box (adds 10-15% in value)

The Internet has matured into a very valuable asset for collectors over the past five years. Just about everyone has heard about eBay™ by now, and this chapter will supply an overview and some buying and selling tips for using online auctions. But the world of online Steiff collecting does not stop with eBay™ as there are several sites dedicated exclusively to Steiff advocates.

A good first stop on your journey is **www.steiffusa.com** where you will find a comprehensive catalog as well as information and photos for recent releases and limited editions. In the "Steiff Collection" section, listings for several teddy bear hospitals as well as some retailers near you can be found. The "Button in the Ear" section contains some background information on Margarete Steiff, the company she started, and collecting in general. Be sure to check out "90 Years of Button in the Ear," a timeline that details the evolution of this popular collectible. You can also join a Steiff club from this site.

Are you interested in a free online price guide for Steiff collectibles? Look no further than **www.collectorvalues.com** where over 5,000 items with prices are provided as well as over 1,500 photos. You can search the site by keyword or by Steiff EAN number. A high value, which is based on dealer asking price, and a medium value, based on typical auction value average, is given. Keep in mind that if you use a common keyword like "bear," your search will take a long time and will return many results. Try to narrow your search by using the Steiff EAN number or less common words like "cinnamon" or "panda."

Some collectors prefer to use message boards to buy and sell rather than use an online auction. Most message boards are free, but they typically don't draw as much traffic or interest as an eBay™ auction does. If you want to explore this avenue, point your browser to **www.worldcollectorsnet.com/steiff/index.html** where you will find not only a Steiff trading board, but a Steiff discussion board as well. Message boards, even if you do not use them to trade, are good places to learn more about your favorite collectibles. If you do want to post an item for sale or make a comment, click on the link for one of the boards. Then click "Post Message" which appears near the top of each board.

Some avid Steiff collectors create their own sites to connect with and assist other Steiff friends. An example of this can be found at **labeck.tripod.com/teddy5.htm** where you can share stories on a message board, buy and sell with online classified ads, visit a chat room for Steiff collectors, and find links to dozens more Steiff web sites.

Lifelong collector, Carolyn B. Cook, contemplates a Steiff purchase on eBay™. Carolyn has authored books about doll collecting and advocates cautiously using the internet as an educational, fun, and potentially profitable tool.

Beyond the web pages already mentioned, you could find more sites—many of them private Steiff dealers—by doing a search from one of the major search engines. Point your browser to one of these search engines, type the word Steiff in the blank box, and click on "Go" or "Search" depending on which site you use. A list of some of the better-known search engines is as follows:

www.altavista.com
www.go.com
www.google.com
www.lycos.com
www.northernlight.com
www.yahoo.com

For most collectors, nothing beats the excitement of finding and bidding on the object of their desire at an online auction, and no online auction has the customer base of eBay™. First conceived in 1995 by a husband for his wife to have a way to trade Pez dispensers online, eBay™ has grown into an enormous repository of anything from common household items to cars and houses. Each year eBay™ grows while other auction sites go out of business.

Avid Steiff collector, Mimi Hiscox, surrounded by a selection of Steiff bears and animals purchased on eBay™. Mimi is very selective of her online purchases. She mainly watches eBay™ for Steiff items she has not been able to find at teddy bear and toy shows. *Photograph by George Hiscox.*

You can find the eBay™ listings for Steiff by clicking on the *Toys & Bean Bag Plush* category of the main menu at **www.ebay.com**. Once clicked, a chart of subcategories appears and you will find Steiff under the *Plush* category. There will typically be 350 or more Steiff items for you to bid on should you choose to do so.

Because Steiff has it's own category on eBay, it's easy to browse for specific Steiff items. You can also perform searches within just the Steiff category instead of having to search all of eBay™ and getting a lot of irrelevant listings returned. Once you are in the listings section of the Steiff category, look at the top of the page for the "Search" box in the right-hand corner. Under the search box are two smaller boxes you can check. One will read "Search only in Toys, Bean Bag Plush" and the other will read "Search titles and descriptions." Check both small boxes by clicking on the box itself, and then type a keyword into the search box for maximum effectiveness.

Anyone can browse the eBay™ listings, but to buy or sell you must register. The only requirement is that you be 18 years of age. You'll find a link to the registration section on the eBay™ home page. Registering is easy and involves little more than filling out an online form with your name, address, primary phone and e-mail address, and reading and accept-

ing the eBay™ User Agreement. A confirming e-mail will be automatically sent to the e-mail address you register, and you can then use the information contained in that message to complete the registration process.

It's important to note that beyond the basic information you must give during the registration process, there will be questions about your collecting interests, age, etc. These are optional questions that you do not need to answer. Several internet businesses make a living buying and selling personal information to companies and individuals that you probably do not want to profile you. While eBay™ is not one of these companies, it's a good habit to not give out personal information. As the internet continues to mature, privacy will become one of the most controversial issues for web surfers. Never divulge more than is required. For this reason it's also advisable to check the box that says "Register using SSL," which adds an extra measure of security by submitting your information through what is known as a "secure server."

Once registered, you are free to place bids. You will find that bidding is also quite easy—so easy in fact that you would do well to keep an eye on how much you spend. Bidding can be habit forming! When you find an item in which you are interested and you want to place a bid, simply click on the "Bid Paddle" at the left side of the listing page. Type a dollar amount (no dollar sign necessary) into the box that says "Your Maximum Bid" and then click the box that says "Review Bid." On the ensuing page, type in your User ID and password and then click "Place Bid."

Three things can happen when you place your bid. Number one (and the one you want to have happen) is that a message will come back that says, "Congratulations, you are the high bidder." You'll own the item when the auction ends unless somebody else outbids you. The second thing that might happen is a message that says, "You are the high bidder, but the seller's reserve has not been met." This means the seller has placed a reserve price or minimum on this item and is not obligated to sell it until his/her reserve is met. You can, if you want to, place another higher bid at this time to see if your new bid meets the reserve price. However, it's better to place a bid for the maximum you are willing to spend from the beginning because of a system eBay™ uses called proxy bidding, which we will look at momentarily. The third thing that might happen is that the message will say, "You have been outbid." How did somebody else outbid you that fast? Proxy bidding.

Proxy bidding is, simply stated, placing your highest bid and having eBay™ place your subsequent bids for you. Let's go back to the example where you place a bid and immediately get a message saying you were outbid. We will pretend you are bidding on a Steiff Possy the Squirrel from the 1980s. The seller has specified an opening bid of $5.00 minimum. Bidder A has already bid on Possy so the current bid amount is $5.00. You place a bid of $8.00 and are immediately outbid. This is because Bidder A actually placed a bid of $15.00, the maximum amount they are willing to spend. eBay™ knows the seller's minimum is $5.00 and places Bidder A's bid for that amount while setting aside the balance. When you place your bid for $8.00, eBay™ uses more of the money set aside for Bidder A so that he/she remains the high bidder at $8.00. The current bid amount will be advanced so that the next person to place a bid will have to bid more than $8.00.

In addition, we should discuss fraud. As internet auctions grow in popularity, internet auction fraud is increasing dramatically. There are some things you can and should do to reduce your risk.

1. Read the description twice. Make sure you understand the important facts about the items on which you bid, particularly the condition. Reading through the description twice, and sometimes three times, helps identify things you might have missed.

2. E-mail sellers with questions. Some people do not describe their merchandise very well. Make sure you understand the description.

3. Insist on photos. Would you purchase merchandise from a catalog without seeing a photo of what you were buying? Probably not, and you should not buy from an internet auction without photos either. While not completely definitive in assessing condition, photos are a great help.

4. Read feedback profiles. Internet auctions provide a way for buyers and sellers to leave feedback for each other after a transaction is completed. Before you bid on an item, check the seller's feedback. If there are more than five negative comments, do not bid.

5. If you decide you want to sell items as well as buy, there is one more registration step you must perform. eBay™ requires members to place a credit card on file before they will allow you to sell. This helps stream line the process of paying auction fees and commissions as your payments are automatically charged against your credit card each month. Do not be afraid to submit your credit card information to eBay™ as the information is processed on a secure server. To my knowledge no one has ever had credit card information stolen due to this registration process.

While buying is free, there are certain fees associated with selling on eBay™. These fees are tied into the opening bid and/or reserve price you set. They can be as low as $0.25 for items with starting bids of less than $10.00 with no reserve. Fees for higher priced items usually fall in the $2.00-$3.00 range, and there are options such as "Featured Auction" that can be much more expensive. You'll have to

A selection of rare Steiff items purchased on eBay™ by Steiff collector Mimi Hiscox (preceding illustration). *Peck* Cough Goblin. Circa 1959. 4in (10cm); FF button. Purchased on eBay™ June, 2000 for $257.77. Today's Market value–$1,000 and up. Fox Terrier Dog. Circa 1915. 10in (25cm); FF button. Purchased on eBay™ August, 1999 for $89. Today's market value–$800 and up. School Girl Doll. Circa 1910. 11in (28cm); FF button; all original with satchel. Purchased on eBay™ June, 2000 for $257.47. Today's market value–$900 and up. Bear Rattle. Circa 1920. 5in (13cm); gold mohair (worn); FF button; rattle encased in torso. Purchased on eBay™ December 1999 for $186.43. Today's market value–$600 and up.

decide if the value you receive from these options is worth the added expense. One option that has proven quite popular is the Gallery, a section where buyers can browse photos instead of the text listings. Adding your photo to the Gallery costs just $0.25, and gives you added exposure to "window shoppers." A final fee commission is also charged on the final price of the item you sell. The commission structure starts out at 5% and decreases as the bid price goes higher. It is important to note that these fees are dramatically less than your local house would charge you for selling the same items.

Speaking of photos, how do you take them and how do you get them to display online? The easiest way is with a digital camera available at most retail outlets and costing anywhere from $250.00 to over $1,000.00. If you're in the market for a digital camera and have an idea of what you want, you can probably find it on eBay™ for less money than buying it retail.

Another way to get photos into digital format is to take them with your film camera and scan the photos on a color scanner. Color scanners today sell for as little as $60.00 and produce acceptable quality for eBay™ photos. Before you run out and buy one though, keep in mind that with this method you must buy film, take the entire roll, have it developed, and then do the scanning. There is more time and money required than the point-and-click ease of a digital camera.

Once you have your photos in a digital form suitable for internet use (JPEG or GIF format), you can upload them to your Internet Service Provider's server or use one of the photo posting services online. If you already pay for internet access, you likely have some server space reserved. Call your ISP and ask them to recommend software for you to be able to upload photos. They will also help you learn the process if they have a good tech support group.

You can also use one of the free picture hosting services online, such as **www.auctionwatch.com** or **www.honesty.com**. Both offer a myriad of services to auction users in addition to free picture hosting. If you work from a Macintosh computer, you may want to try **www.macrules.com** instead.

When you are finally ready to list your item for sale, click on the "Sell" box from the eBay™ home page. You'll have to pick a category in which to place your item, write a description, and furnish the internet address information of your photo(s) as well as supply pricing and shipping information. All of this is done from an online form, which makes it fairly easy to accomplish after some practice, trial and error. You'll always see a representation of your listing as others will see it and have the opportunity to make changes before you actually finalize it and start the auction.

The internet can enhance the fun of Steiff collecting dramatically. Get online, learn, and have some fun!

The information supplied in this section is a brief synopsis of some of the tools, tricks, and tips for using online auctions taken from *The ABCs of Collecting Online* by Ray Boileau. For an in-depth study of using the internet to buy, sell, and collect, including many more tips, tricks, and strategies, copies of this landmark book can be ordered from Hobby House Press by calling 1-800-554-1447.

BEWARE OF FAKES

As with any collectible item of value, there are some unscrupulous people who insist on offering merchandise that is not what it seems. You can protect yourself from this unfortunate circumstance by studying your facts and learning as much as you can about bears and soft toys. Always purchase from reputable vendors! Get to know reliable and well-known dealers. Rely on referrals from professionals and friends.

Using this Book

Please remember that the prices here are only a guide. Each price listed is for the current retail value of the Steiff bear or animal. The data for pricing was gathered during 1998-2000 from antique shops, shows, auctions, doll and teddy bear specialty shops, conventions, advertisements in periodicals, lists from teddy bear and doll dealers, purchases and sales reported by both collectors and dealers, and research online. Prices are not absolute and correspond only to the particular bears and animals shown here. There may be fluctuations in market value according to geographic region and cycles in other conditions such as popularity and demand. Neither the author nor the publisher assumes responsibility for any losses, which may occur as a result of following this guide.

Please keep in mind that no price guide, no matter how complete and thorough, can be the last word. It should only be an aid. The final decision is up to you. You alone know the meaning of your decision. Perhaps he completes a set or his face is particularly soulful or she carries the name of your first child. You alone can make that price decision while examining the specific piece in question.

Before buying, do a lot of looking and comparing. Don't be afraid to ask questions. There is only one thing Steiff collectors love more than their bears and that is talking about them. It's the best way for you to learn and the finest way to get the most value for your purchase.

Identifying Your Steiff

Although identifying your Steiff is quite complex, the more experience you have, the easier it becomes.

There are specific areas that offer consistent identifying characteristics.
1. body shape
2. limb length
3. muzzle
4. hump (or lack of it)
5. construction and materials used for fur, eyes, pads and stuffing
6. design, stitching of nose, mouth and claws
7. position of eyes

Though these particular features have changed over the years, they can help you identify your Steiff bear or animal with just a few exceptions. Here are some tips to get you started.

Buttons (affixed to left ear)

1904/05
- Elephant button
- Blank button
- Small metal blank button with two-prong attachment

1905-48
- Printed (raised) STEIFF button with F underscored on metal button with two-prong attachment

1948-50
- Blank blue button (grays with age)

c.1950
- Printed (raised) STEIFF button without F underscored on metal button with two-prong attachment

1950-c.1970
- Raised STEIFF in script on metal button with two-prong attachment

1970-1977
- Incised STEIFF in script on chrome button, riveted in ear

1980-present
- Brass button (slightly larger in size than earlier buttons) with incised STEIFF in script; riveted in ear

2001
- Gold plated button; riveted in ear. Special limited editions

Chest Tags

c. 1908
- White paper S.L. (special paper woven with fibers on all paper labels); Number indicates exact look of animal as to posture, covering and height (in centimeters)

c. 1910-26
- White paper S.L.; More information added to label *geschutz* (protected by law) Germany Importe d' Allemage (made in Germany)

c. 1925-34/35
- Red stock paper label

1926-28
- White paper circle with metal edge

1928-50
- Paper circle with red outer rim, beige center and yellow angular bear's head at bottom (from 1984 reproduced for the "1928-1950 Replica Series")

c. 1934-50
- Yellow stock paper label

c. 1947-53
- An extra white woven label "Made in US-Zone Germany" was sewn into the seam of the body

1950-72
- Paper circle with red outer rim, beige center and yellow smiling bear's head at bottom (from 1983 reproduced for "1950s-1960s Replica Editions") animal and Steiff logo labels
- Stock Labels (affixed by button to left ear)

c. 1960-72
- Yellow coated linen label; style of information has changed; place designated for price

c. 1977-80
- Yellow coated linen; style of information is the same; slash now used instead of comma; same design used today; material differs over time

1980-82
- White woven S.L. used for limited editions

1982-87
- Yellow cloth weave S.L.

1986-present
- White printed ribbon S.L. used for limited editions

1986-present
- Yellow printed ribbon S.L.

Materials

1904
- Mohair

1919-20
- Brennessel (nettleplant derivative); shortage of quality materials due to WWI forced substitution of less expensive materials: paper plush (wood-fiber derivative material)

1947-48
- Mohair supply halted from English supplier due to WWII; synthetic silk plush used instead

1949
- Mohair

1955
- Draylon; used until end of the 1970's

Stuffing

- In early bears, excelsior (wood shavings, crush to touch) or a mixture of excelsior and Kapok were used.

1955
- Foam rubber stuffing

1960
- Foam rubber and foam flakes (disintegrated over time); pre-formed foam articles introduced end of 1960's

1970
- Soft synthetic stuffing

Eyes

- Shoe-button eyes were used first.

1908
- Glass eyes introduced

1920
- Clear glass painted on the back with metal loop

1960
- Transition from glass to plastic attached with thread or starlock-disc (security-eye)

Voice Box

1905-07
- Squeeze type voice box

1908
- Automatic (tilt-type) voice box

Pads

1904
- Felt pads

1970
- Rippled woven velvet

1976
- Jersey knit

Embroidered Claws

1904-05
- Five claws

1905-present
- Four claws

Key for Steiff Bears and Animals

§ f.j. indicates "fully jointed" (jointed arms and legs; swivel head)

§ n.j. indicates "non-jointed" (arms and legs are not jointed; stationary head)

§ e.s. indicates "excelsior stuffing" (wood shavings)

§ k.s. indicates "kapok stuffing" (silky fiber covering the seeds of the tropical kapok tree which grows in Africa, the East Indies, and tropical parts of America)

§ s.s. indicates "soft stuffing" (stuffed with various soft materials, i.e., cotton, acrylic)

§ N.P.A. indicates "no price available" (not enough examples sold to establish price)

§ S.A. indicates "still available"

§ FF button indicates "STEIFF" name in capital letters with F underscored on pewter colored metal button

§ R.S.B. indicates Steiff name is "raised script" on pewter-colored shiny metal button

§ I.B. indicates Steiff name is "incised" in script on shiny chrome button

§ B.B. indicates Steiff name is incised in script on large "brass button"

§ S.L. indicates "stock label" is attached by ear button

§ C.T. indicates "chest tag"

1877
- Margarete Steiff opens company to make felt clothes

1880
- Margarete Steiff adapts little felt elephant pin cushion; First animal toys introduced

1892
- First Steiff catalog
- Bears standing on all fours or erect (non-jointed); 5in (13cm) and 8in (20cm)
- Bears on iron wheels introduced

1893
- Business registered as "Felt Toy Company"

1897-1906
- Margarete Steiff's five nephews join company: Richard, Paul, Franz, Hugo, and Otto

1897
- Richard Steiff represents company at Leipzig Trade Fair

1898
- **Polar Bear**, **Brown Bear** and **Ride-on Bear** on metal frame
- **Roly Poly Bear** (standing bear on conical wooden base) in brown burlap

1902
- Jointed doll introduced; Comic figures with arms and legs jointed through body by twine that was fastened with knot
- Richard Steiff attends Wieser's American Animal Circus at Memmingerthorplatz to see Barribal Bears found throughout North America (October 26)
- Richard Steiff conceives idea for toy animals through study of bears in circus; animals made with moveable limbs; used animals like bears and monkeys because they could stand upright and possessed more "human" qualities
- First jointed bear ("**Barle**") arrives on the scene
- **Bär 55 PB** (first jointed bear); **Monkey 60 PB** (first jointed monkey).
- Number indicated size of animal in a "sitting" position (55 cm, 60 cm); "P" stands for plush; "B" stands for for *beweglich* (jointed). Bär characteristics: very plump, resembles real bear; made of dark brown mohair; arms and legs attached to the body by twine that was fastened with knot on the outside of the stuffing under the plush; No examples in existence, only a photograph in early Steiff catalog

1903   (Spring)
- **Bär 55 PB** introduced at the Leipzig Trade Fair. Brought little attention;
- American buyer Hermann Berg (George Borgfeldt & Co.) ordered 3,000

1904

- **Bär 35 PB** created (Pat. dated March 5, 1904). Richard Steiff modified design of **Bar 55 PB** to create a smaller, appealing bear; Improved twine jointing of arms and legs; Experimented with wire instead of twine, but wires were safety hazard
- Jointing improvements result in "Toys with moveable joints connected inside the body with double wires" under Patent DRGM 242399; Wires now twisted together and covered by stuffing for safety; Bear retains name 35PB
- Franz Steiff sells 12,000 35 PB at the World's Fair in St. Louis
- Margarete and Richard Steiff awarded Gold Medals for industry and effort
- Franz Steiff creates "Button in Ear" concept

1905

- Margarete Steiff sends customers a letter that read "Trademark (i.e. Elephant with "S" shaped trunk). "As of November 1, 1904, I shall identify each article without exception, with a small nickel-plated button in the left ear. Our logo is stamped on these buttons and is legally protected."
- **Bär 28 PB** created. Metal rod jointing (pat. dated June 8, 1905); Characteristics: Firm metal rod passed through body to arms and legs, elephant button, shoe-button eyes, sealing wax nose, horizontal seam at top of head (head stuffed from above)
- **Bär 35 PAB** produced. "A" stands for *angescheibt* (disc-jointed); Patent registered February 2, 1905; Known as Richard Steiff's "bear-doll;" Characteristics: moveable joints (cardboard disks held together with metal pin), stitched nose, sweeter rounder face, thinner body, a real teddy bear! (Richard's personal model is in the Steiff Archives and is often referred to as "Gray Richard" (please refer to page 6); He was called "Barle" on the price list and was offered in seven sizes from 10in (25cm) to 45in (114cm) tall. He came in dark brown, white, and light brown fur. By 1909, he was also offered in gold.

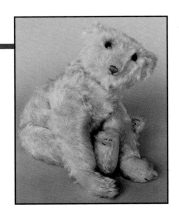

1906

- **Humpty Dumpty**. Based on nursery rhyme character from "Alice in Wonderland" by British author Lewis Carol; Available in three sizes Company registers as Margarete Steiff GmbH (July 6); Margarete Steiff's nephews, Paul, Richard and Franz-Josef, are managing directors

1907

- Factory renamed "The Margarete Steiff Toy Factory Ltd." 974,000 teddy bears produced
- **Hot Water Bottle Bear** (90 produced). Characteristics: Metal hot water bottle concealed in tummy; Opening is closed by strong ribbon lacing around hooks on either side of tummy **Holland Rabbit**. Franz Steiff designed mechanism simulating natural movement of the ears

1907/08

- Dressed bears introduced

1908

- Steiff's "**Bärle**" (named for Steiff's jointed bear) becomes "*Teddy-Bär*"
- **Muzzle Bears**. Produced in white and light to dark brown in ten different sizes
- **Somersault Bear**. Mechanical bear; Tumbles when arms are wound
- Glass eyes introduced in teddy bears

1908/1917
• **Golliwog.** Rendition of main character in Florence Uptown's books.

1909
• **Margarete Steiff** dies shortly before her 62nd birthday (May 9)
• **Roly-Poly Bear.** Made of mohair with jointed head and arms and roly-poly body

1910/15
• **Pantom Bear.** 605 pieces produced in sizes 13-½ in (35cm) and 16-½ in (40 cm)
• **Pantom Doll.** "By oscillating turns of a wooden fork in the wrist and by moving forward according Pantom will walk in the most lifelike manner."

1911/1915
• **Snak** (Dwarf)

1911/1930
• **Snik** (Dwarf)

1912
• **Black Bears (Mourning Bear).** Created in memory of the Titanic that sank on April 14, 1912
• **Hand Puppets**

1912/1917
• **Puss-In-Boots.** 1,400 pieces produced; Three sizes

1912/1950
• **Record Peter.** Popular record series produced in a variety of animals and character dolls; Figure seated on sturdy metal chassis with four wooden wheels and pair of bellows fitted to rear axle for automatic sound effect; When pulled, figure moves back and forth; Looks like animal is steering itself

1912
• **Tige.** Rendition of Buster brown's bull terrier "Tige"

1913
• **Puck** (Dwarf)

1920
• Conveyor belt system introduced

1925
• **Molly Dog**

1926/28
• **Teddy Clown.** Bear with felt clown hat and neck ruff

1927
• **Bully** (French Bulldog)

1927/1931
• **Jack Rabbit.** Character from American children's book published by Grosset and Dunlop Books; 2,780 produced

1925/31
- **Pip**. Character bully dog with googlie eyes developed from A.B. Payne's cartoons featured in the *Daily Mirror* newspaper.

1928/1930
- **Petsy**. Bear cub. Characteristics: oversized, poseable ears; fitted with wires, red or black-stitched nose and claws; blue glass eyes

1928
- **Treff**. Created from English dog "Dismal Desmond"
- Musical bears and animals. Swiss music box encased in torso of animal. Tag attached to animal's tummy read, "Squeeze me gently here then music you will hear."

1931/1936
- **Mickey Mouse; Minnie Mouse**

1929/1950
- **Teddy Baby**. "Life-like model of comical young bear whose friendly face speaks volumes." Produced in twelve sizes 3in (8cm) to 20in (51cm) with open and closed mouth; Made in mohair, artificial, and wool plush

1930/1936
- **Dicky Bear**. Advertised as "A new improved and less expensive Steiff teddy bear." Produced in white, blonde, or gold in sizes ranging from 6in (15cm) to 16in (14cm). Characteristics: smiling mouth; gold version's nose stitched with black thread while white and blonde versions' stitched with brown thread

1933
- **Drinking Cat**. Rubber ball encased in torso; Pressing body, cat laps up liquid through thin pipe

1935/39
- **Circus Bear**. Produced in 12-½ in (32cm); Mechanical head moves in circular motion when tail is turned

1938
- **Panda**. Ruth Harkness turned America into a panda-loving nation when she brought Su-Lin to Chicago's Brookfield Zoo in 1938. Steiff continued to produce pandas until the 1960s

1951
- **Zotty**

1952
- **Nimrod Teddy**. Dressed in hunter's costume; Four different outfits

1953
- Mechanical neck movement (head turns in circular motion when tail is turned)

1955
- Teddy bears produced in Draylon

1980
- In celebration of its 100th year, Jubilee Steiff introduces special editions and replicas

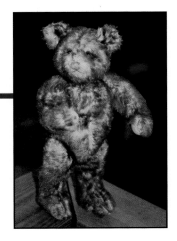

Left: These examples of teddy bears produced by Steiff from 1905 to 1970 will help you learn to recognize the characteristics of their bears from different eras. (Left) Circa 1905. 25in (64cm); long curly apricot-colored mohair; large black button eyes; f.j.; e.s. and k.s.; beige felt pads reinforced with black felt and cardboard; squeeze-type cry box; FF button. Characteristics of this early realistic bear design are wide head; long snout; big hump on back; arms and legs are plump at joints tapering down to large paws and feet. When sitting, arms extend over feet. Squeeze-type cry box. Cardboard and various colors of felt reinforce the pads on the feet. Four stitched floss claws (before 1905 five stitched claws were applied). Vertically stitched nose (16in [41cm] and larger were stitched vertically, 14in [36cm] and smaller were horizontally stitched). CONDITION: Good. PRICE: $13,000–up. (Center left) Circa 1950. 15in (31cm); white mohair; glass eyes; f.j.; e.s.; tilt-type cry box; R.S.B. The realistic bear design is now completely replaced by a very trim-looking design. Hump is almost gone. Arms are shorter with very little curve. Body is straight and narrow. Legs and feet still have nice shape but are shorter. Stuffing is packed extremely tightly. Tilt-type cry box. CONDITION: Good. PRICE: $1,000–up. (Center right) Circa 1970. 25in (64cm); silky caramel-colored mohair; short mohair inset snout; glass eyes; f.j.; e.s.; tilt-type cry box; I.S.B. Bear has now developed a chunky appearance. Head is fatter and nose is much shorter. Hardly any hump is visible. A shorter fat arm with less shape is now used along with a similarly shaped leg. Pads are now synthetic material. Muzzle is now shaved. Stuffing is packed extremely tightly. You can really notice the change in the design of the Steiff bears from this era. Typical characteristics of Steiff teddy bears are hand-sewn finishing seam usually at tummy. CONDITION: Excellent. PRICE: $250–up. (Right) Circa 1915. 16in (41cm); gold silky mohair; glass eyes; f.j.; e.s.; felt pads; FF button. Elongated arms and legs are still evident. However, this design is slightly more tailored and glass eyes are now being used (introduced in 1908). CONDITION: Excellent. PRICE: $5,000–up.

Above: An outstanding display of miniature Steiff teddy bears from 1907–1950 is exhibited at the Puppenhausmuseum, in Basel, Switzerland. CONDITION: Mint to excellent. PRICE: $500–$2,000 (each). *Courtesy Puppenhausmuseum. Basel.*

Top left: Somersault Bear. Circa 1908. 10in (25cm); honey-colored mohair; shoe-button eyes; f.j.; e.s.; FF button; white S.L. When arms are wound in circular motion it activates clockwork mechanism, which creates tumbling motion. Original box fastened with FF buttons. The somersault mechanism was also installed in a monkey and in an elephant. CONDITION: Mint. PRICE: $20,000–up. *Courtesy Barbara Baldwin.*

Bottom left: Bear. Circa 1910. 13in (33cm); golden mohair; shoe-button eyes; f.j.; e.s.; FF button. *Putzi*. Circa 1935. 8-¾in (22cm); grayish-white mohair; large shoe-button eyes; red felt tongue; n.j. arms and legs; swivel head; e.s. CONDITION: Worn. PRICE: Bear approximately $900. **Putzi** did not meet reserve. Sold at Horst Poestgens, Germany 1988 auction. *Courtesy Horst Poestgens, Auctioneer, Germany.*

Top right: Bear. Circa 1907. 13in (33cm); golden beige mohair; shoe-button eyes; f.j.; e.s. *Teddy B* playsuit made from the 1907 Home Pattern Company "Teddy Bear Outfit" pattern consisting of "Two Piece Play Suit", "Pajamas" and "Rough Rider Suit" (left). CONDITION: Fair. PRICE: $2,000-$2,500 (Bear with outfit and pattern). *Courtesy Mimi Hiscox.*

Bottom right: American toy dealer Richard Wright nearly set a world record price for a teddy bear at Sotheby's May 15, 1987 auction when he purchased the bear on the left. He bought the 21-½in (55cm) rare white, mint condition Steiff muzzle bear, circa 1913, for the sum of £8,800 (approximately $15,114). The similar, but smaller, Steiff bear on the right sold at the same auction for £6,050 (approximately $10,700). Approximate price in today's market, $20,000–up (each). Richard specializes in rare and collectible antique dolls. Surrounding the bears is a Steiff soldier (circa 1913) and highly desirable early 1900s bisque dolls. *Courtesy Richard Wright. Photograph by Ann Jackson.*

Above: The rare early 1900s large size Steiff bears are highly sought-after by teddy bear collectors. They are especially desirable in this pristine condition with great facial appeal. Bear. Circa 1908. 28in (71cm); rich golden-colored mohair; shoe-button eyes; f.j.; e.s.; FF button. CONDITION: Mint. PRICE: $28,000–up. *Courtesy Steve Estes. Photograph by Alvin Gee.*

Above: Steiff Muzzle Teddy Bears were premiered at the Leipzig Trade Fair in 1908. They were produced in white and dark to light brown mohair in 10 different sizes. Muzzle Bears. Circa 1910. 8in–20in (20cm–51cm); white, beige and brown tones of mohair; large button eyes; leather muzzles; f.j.; e.s. CONDITION: Mint to Excellent. PRICE: $7,000–$25,000 (each). *Courtesy Puppenhausmuseum. Basel.*

Left: Bear (Left). Circa 1908. 13in (32cm); gray mohair (was originally brown); shoe-button eyes; e.s.; FF button. CONDITION: Good. PRICE: $4,500–up. Bear (Right). Circa 1908. 14in (36cm); pale gold mohair; shoe-button eyes; f.j.; e.s;. FF button; remnants of white label. Wearing old *Teddy G* and *Teddy B* outfits. CONDITION: Good. PRICE: $5,000–up. *Private Collection.*

Far left: Pantom Bear. Circa 1910. 14in (36cm); gold mohair; shoe-button eyes; loosely jointed arms, legs and swivel head; e.s.; FF button. Extremely rare. Produced from 1910 until 1918 in two sizes, 14in (36cm) and 16in (41cm). Strings are attached to loops of string fastened to head, back and each wrist and leg. Bear is activated like a puppet by moving wooden handle on which all strings are fastened. A Pantom doll and a Pantom Chimp also were produced during the same time period. CONDITION: Excellent. PRICE: $15,000–up. *Courtesy Private Collection.*

Top right: Bear with muzzle. Circa 1910. 16in (40cm); gold mohair; shoe-button eyes; leather muzzle; f.j.; e.s . Rare. CONDITION: Excellent. PRICE: $15,000–up. *Courtesy Puppenhausmuseum. Basel.*

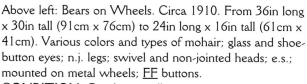

Above left: Bears on Wheels. Circa 1910. From 36in long x 30in tall (91cm x 76cm) to 24in long x 16in tall (61cm x 41cm). Various colors and types of mohair; glass and shoe-button eyes; n.j. legs; swivel and non-jointed heads; e.s.; mounted on metal wheels; FF buttons.
CONDITION: Good to excellent.
PRICE: 9in (23cm) high $600–$800
          11in (28cm) high $800–$1,000
          16in (41cm) high $1,500–$2,000
          22in (56cm) high $2,500–$3,000
          30in (76cm) high $3,500–up
Rare colors may command higher prices.

Above right: *Roly Poly* Bear. Circa 1912. 7in (16cm); beige mohair; shoe-button eyes; jointed arms; swivel head; e.s. CONDITION: Fair. PRICE: $5,000–up. *Courtesy Puppenhausmuseum. Basel.*

Left: Black Bears. Circa 1912. 10in–16in (25cm–41cm); black mohair; glass eyes; f.j.; e.s.; <u>FF</u> button. Extremely rare. CONDITION: Excellent. PRICE: $18,000–$40,000 (each). *Courtesy Puppenhausmuseum. Basel*

Above left: Black Bear. Circa 1912. 20in (51cm); black silky mohair; shoe-button eyes backed with red felt; "center seam" head; f.j.; e.s.; <u>FF</u> button. Extremely rare. It appears approximately 12 black bears were produced with the desirable center seam. Note the appeal and contrast of the red felt backing behind the eyes compared to the bear on the right (see top photo). CONDITION: Excellent. PRICE: approximately $41,000. Sold at Sotheby's May 1990 auction. *Private collection.*

Above right: Bear. Circa 1912. 16in (40cm); black cloth coat; shoe-button eyes with red felt background; nose embroidered in light pinkish beige; f.j.; e.s. Extremely rare. CONDITION: Good. PRICE: $23,000–up. *Courtesy Puppenhausmuseum. Basel..*

Far left: Polar Bears with neck mechanism. Circa 1913. (Left) 13in (33cm); (Right) 18in (46cm) (in sitting position); white mohair; shoe-button eyes; e.s. Head moves in circular motion when tail is moved. CONDITION: Excellent. PRICE: 13in (33cm) $5,000–up; 18in (46cm) $6,500–up. *Private collection.*

Top right: Bear on Wheels. Circa 1915. 16in tall x 24in long (41cm x 61cm); dark brown mohair; glass eyes; n.j. legs; stationary head; e.s.; wooden wheels. Note metal pull handle. Steiff introduced animals on wooden wheels in approximately 1914. CONDITION: Excellent. PRICE: $2,500–up. Bear. Circa 1915. 18in (46cm); light gold; glass eyes; f.j.; e.s.; FF button. CONDITION: Excellent. PRICE: $6,000–up. *Private collection.*

Above left: *Bear Dolly*. Circa 1913. 12in (30cm); white mohair head; red mohair body; shoe-button eyes; neck ruff; f.j.; e.s.; FF button. *Bear Dolly* was the novelty of the 1913 Leipzig Spring Trade Fair. Manufactured between 1913 and 1918 in three different sizes. CONDITION: Very good. PRICE: $20,000–up. *Courtesy Puppenhausmuseum. Basel.*

Above right: Bear. Circa 1915. 15in (38cm); long wavy white mohair; glass eyes; f.j.; e.s.; FF button. CONDITION: Mint. PRICE: $7,000–up. *Courtesy Deborah and Donald Ratliff.*

Right: Price guide for Steiff's basic teddy bear design produced from 1910 to 1930 in mohair with glass eyes; f.j.; e.s.; <u>FF</u> button..
PRICES:

	Mint Condition	Good Condition	Fair Condition
10in (25cm)	$1,800–up	$1,000–up	$750–up
16in (41cm)	$5,500–up	$3,000–up	$1,500–up
20in (51cm)	$8,000–up	$5,000–up	$2,500–up
24in (61cm)	$12,500–up	$6,000–up	$4,000–up
28in (71cm)	$16,000–up	$7,500–up	$5,000–up

Rare colors and extra appealing facial expressions command higher prices. *Photograph courtesy Judy and Lee Day.*

Left: Bear (Left). Circa 1907. 29in (74cm); white mohair; large button eyes; f.j.; e.s.; <u>FF</u> button. CONDITION: Excellent. PRICE: $25,000–up. Bear (Center) (movable head mechanism). Circa 1933. 9in (23cm); dark brown mohair; short beige mohair inset snout; glass eyes; n.j.; e.s.; <u>FF</u> button. Turning tail moves head in circular motion. CONDITION: Fair. PRICE: $2,500–up. Bear (Right). Circa 1920. 28in (71cm); gold mohair; glass eyes; "center seam" head; f.j.; e.s.; <u>FF</u> button. CONDITION: Excellent. PRICE: $12,000–up.

Right: Bear. 1920. 16in (41cm); gray (originally brown) mohair; glass eyes; f.j.; e.s.; <u>FF</u> button. CONDITION: Excellent. PRICE: $6,500–up.

Right: "Paper" Plush Bear. Circa 1919. 17in (43cm); brown-gray cotton cloth; shoe-button eyes; f.j.; e.s. Rare. Manufactured between 1919 and 1921. This is a woven material from a plant called "die brennessel" (nettle) and paper plush. It is not very durable. Steiff used nettle fiber during World War I when materials were scarce. CONDITION: Excellent. PRICE: $20,000-up. *Courtesy Puppenhausmuseum. Basel.*

Left: Bear (Prototype). 1920's. 14in (36cm); red and blue mohair; gold felt paw pads; one blue glass eye, one brown glass eye; f.j. e.s. PRICE: DM 160,000 (approximately $86,758). Sold at the 3rd Steiff Festival in Giengen in 1999. *Courtesy David Douglass.*

Right: Bear (Left). Circa 1920. 10in (25cm); blonde mohair; glass eyes; f.j.; e.s. CONDITION: Fair. PRICE: $800-$900. Bear (Right). Circa 1908. 27-½in (70cm); long wavy gray-brown mohair; glass eyes; f.j.; e.s. CONDITION: Excellent. PRICE: $16,000-up. *Photograph courtesy Horst Poestgens, auctioneer, Germany.*

Right: Bear (Left). Circa 1920. 8in (20cm); worn beige mohair; shoe-button eyes; f.j.; e.s.; <u>FF</u> button. CONDITION: Worn. PRICE: $500–$700. Bear (Right). Circa 1920. 24in (61cm); long white mohair; glass eyes; brown stitched nose; mouth and claws; f.j.; e.s.; <u>FF</u> button. CONDITION: Excellent. PRICE: $9,000–up. *Photograph courtesy Horst Poestgens, Auctioneer, Germany.*

Left: Hand puppets. Bears. Circa 1920. (Left) white mohair; (Right) gold mohair; shoe-button eyes; n.j. head and arms; e.s. head. CONDITION: Mint. PRICE: (Left) $3,500–up;. (Right) $2,000–up. *Courtesy David Douglass.*

Right: Record Teddy Bears. Circa 1920–1930. 5-¾–10in (15cm–25cm). Various colors of mohair, fully jointed bears with shoe-button and glass eyes mounted on metal frames with wooden wheels. All bears have printed STEIFF button with F underscored. Originally introduced in 1912 with a monkey, Record Peter, the popular Record series was produced with a variety of animals and character dolls until 1950. CONDITION: Excellent. PRICE: $5,000–$8,000 each. Rare colors command higher prices. *Private collection.*

Right: Bear. Circa 1920. 15-½in (40cm); pale gold mohair; glass eyes; f.j.; e.s.; FF button. Steiff Cat. Circa 1910. Worn gray mohair; green glass eyes n.j.; e.s.; FF button. Steiff Hare. Circa 1910. 9-½in (24cm) long; beige felt; glass eyes; red stitched nose and mouth; n.j.; e.s.; FF button. CONDITION: Worn. PRICE: Bear. approximately $1,000; Cat. approximately $250; Hare. approximately $200. Sold at Horst Poestgens October 30, 1998 auction, Germany. *Courtesy Horst Poestgens, Auctioneer, Germany.*

Left: Bear (Left.) Circa 1920. 24in (61cm); glass eyes. Bear (Right). Circa 1920. 26in (66cm); glass eyes; f.j.; e.s. CONDITION: Excellent. PRICE: 24in (61cm) $10,000–up; 26in (66cm) $12,000–up. *Courtesy Ho Phi Le.*

Right: Bear. Circa 1926. 16in (40cm); long pale yellow mohair; oversized glass eyes; brown stitched nose, mouth and claws; f.j.; e.s.; FF button. CONDITION: Good. PRICE: $10,000–up. *Courtesy Puppenhausmuseum. Basel.*

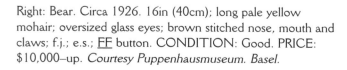

Right: Wiwag with Teddy Bear and Monkey. Circa 1926. Teddy Bear 5-½in (14cm); short gold mohair; small button eyes; f.j.; e.s.; FF button; remnants of a white label. Monkey 5-½in (14cm); brown felt head and body; beige felt face and ears; small button eyes; n.j.; e.s.; FF button; remnants of a white label; metal frame; wooden wheels painted red. Animals see-saw up and down when toy is pulled. Only 330 pieces were made from 1926 to 1928. CONDITION: Mint. PRICE: $10,000–up. *Courtesy Lisa Vought.*

Left: Roly-Droly with Teddy Bear and Monkey. Circa 1926. Teddy Bear. 3in tall x 3in long (8cm x 8cm); caramel-colored plush; small black button eyes; n.j. Animals are attached to the metal frame with wooden wheels. When toy is pulled, the animals turn in circular motion. The original box pictures the various animals Steiff made as a Roly-Droly toy. CONDITION: Mint. PRICE: $10,000–up. *Courtesy Lisa Vought.*

Right: *Teddy Rose.* 1926. 13in (33cm); pale rose pink mohair; large glass eyes; f.j.; e.s.; FF button. CONDITION: Excellent. PRICE: $20,000–up. *Courtesy David Douglass.*

Right: Bear. (Prototype for Teddy Clown). Circa 1925. 24in (61cm); brown mohair; beige mohair snout; glass eyes; f.j.; e.s. Extremely rare. CONDITION: Mint. PRICE: Sold in 1997 at Steiff's auction in Giengen for approximately $100,000. *Private Collection.*

Left: Musical Bear. Circa 1928. 16in (36cm); yellow mohair; glass eyes; rust- colored stitched nose, mouth and claws; f.j.; e.s. Bellows produce music when tummy is squeezed. Originally a paper tag attached to tummy of bear read, "Squeeze me gently here then music you will hear!" Produced between 1928 and 1930. Extremely rare. Steiff produced other musical animals in this series, but they are all IDENTICAL to the animals in the normal Steiff production! The only difference is they contain a bellows music box. CONDITION: Excellent. PRICE: $25,000–up. *Courtesy David Douglas.*

Right: *Petsy* Bears . Circa 1928. 11in (28cm), 17in (43cm), and 20in (51cm): red-brown tipped white mohair; blue glass eyes (bear on right has rare "googlie" eyes); f.j.; s.s. (excelsior and wool); FF button; remnants of red label. Steiff *Petsy* bears are extremely rare, especially with googlie eyes. Characteristics are over-sized posable ears fitted with wires, red stitched nose and claws, and blue glass eyes (backed with white milk glass). However, a brown-eyed *Petsy* with brown stitched nose and claws was also produced. Another distinctive feature is the design of the head. Seams run down from the center, front, back and crosswise from ears to back; V-shaped gusset from center of mouth to neck. This design was a considerable change for Steiff as they had mainly produced the *Richard Steiff* teddy bear design for the past 25 years. Steiff created *Petsy's* head design to resemble a bear cub. Produced in 10 sizes (6in–20in [15cm–51cm]). Production ended in 1930. *Petsy* bears from left to right. CONDITION: Excellent. PRICE: 11in (28cm) $10,000–up; 17in (43cm) $15,000–up; 20in (51cm) "Googlie" eyes $20,000–up. *Private collection.*

Right: Teddy Clowns. Circa 1926. 6in–20in (14cm–51cm); various beige and gold colors of brown-tipped mohair; glass eyes; f.j.; e.s.; FF button; original clown hats and ruffs. CONDITION: Mint to good. PRICE: $3,000–$30,000 (each). Steiff Bears on wheels. Circa 1910. 12in–30in (31cm–76cm); brown burlap; large black button eyes; n.j. legs; swivel head; FF button; metal wheels. CONDITION: Excellent. PRICE: $1,000–$3,500 each. *Courtesy Puppenhausmuseum. Basel.*

Left: Teddy Clown. Bear. Circa 1926. 11in (36cm); pale beige mohair; glass eyes; f.j.; e.s.; FF button; white C.T. reads: "Teddyclown." Felt clown hat with red silk pompoms. Two-colored silk ruff. Rare, especially with C.T. CONDITION: Mint. PRICE: $12,000–up. *Courtesy Barbara Baldwin.*

Right: *Petsy* Teddy Clown. Circa 1926–1928; 15in (38cm); brown-tipped pale beige mohair; glass eyes; "center seam" head; f.j.; excelsior and wool stuffing; prototype; ears set well back; original hat and ruff. Rare. CONDITION: Excellent. PRICE: $26,000–up. *Courtesy Puppenhausmuseum. Basel.*

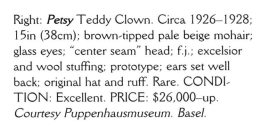

Far left: *Petsy* Musical Bear. Circa 1929. 12in (30cm); brown-tipped mohair; blue glass eyes; f.j.; e.s; squeeze mechanism on side. Extremely rare. CONDITION: Very good. PRICE: $16,000–up. *Courtesy Puppenhausmuseum. Basel.*

Top right: *Teddy Baby.* Circa 1940. 10in (26cm); maize artificial silk plush; glass eyes; f.j.; e.s.; FF button; C.T. CONDITION: Mint. PRICE: $2,000–$2,500. *Courtesy Puppenhausmuseum. Basel.*

Bottom right: *Petsy.* 1928. 13-3/4in (35cm); brass-colored mohair; glass eyes; f.j.; e.s.; FF button. CONDITION: Excellent. PRICE: $10,000–up. *Courtesy David Douglass.*

Bottom left: *Teddy Babies.* Circa 1929. 14in (36cm), 10-½in (27cm), and 7in (18cm); white long silky mohair; short white mohair inset snout and tops of feet; rust-colored pearl cotton nose and claws; glass eyes; "laughing open" felt mouth; f.j.; e.s. 14in (36cm) has FF button with remnants of red label. *Teddy Babies* were mainly produced in dark brown and a cream-colored (maize) mohair. The white mohair is quite rare and very desirable among collectors. *Teddy Baby,* probably Steiff's most humorous bear, was advertised as a "Model of a lifelike comical young bear-cub whose friendly face speaks volumes; may be made to stand upright, or sit, as desired." *Teddy Baby* was also produced with a closed mouth. He was made in mohair, artificial silk, and wool plush. *Teddy Baby* proved so popular he remained in Steiff's program until the late 1950s. He was then reintroduced in 1985. CONDITION: Excellent. PRICE: 7in (18cm) $1,500–up; 10-½in (27cm) $2,500–up; 14in (36cm) $3,500–up. *Private collection.*

Right: *Teddy Babies.* Circa 1930–1940. 8in–25in (20cm–64cm); various colors of mohair; short mohair inset snout and tops of feet; glass eyes; open and closed mouth versions; f.j.; e.s. F̲F̲ button; C.T. CONDITION: Mint to excellent. PRICE: $1,500–$4,500 (each). *Courtesy Puppenhausmuseum. Basel.*

Left: *Teddy Babies.* Circa 1929. (Left) 9-¾in (25cm); (Right) 7-½in (19cm); red-brown mohair with short light beige mohair inset snout; glass eyes; f.j.; e.s.; F̲F̲ button; red label. The popular *Teddy Baby* was produced in white, brown, and maize mohair with a closed and open mouth versions. Closed mouth appears to be more rare. Outfitted in a collar with a bell. Brown and white bears have a red collar. Maize bears have a blue collar. CONDITION: Mint. PRICE: 9-¾in (25cm) $2,000–up; 7-½in (19cm) $1,500–up. *Courtesy Ruth Baum.*

Right: *Dicky* Bear. (Right) Circa 1930. 12in (31cm); white mohair with short mohair plush inset snout; velvet paw pads with painted paw design; glass eyes; f.j.; e.s.; F̲F̲ button; remnants of red label. CONDI- TION: Excellent. PRICE: $14,000–up. *Dicky* Bear (Left). Circa 1930. 9in (23cm); gold mohair with corn-gold short mohair plush inset snout; felt pads; glass eyes; f.j.; e.s.; FF button; remnants of red label. *Dicky* was advertised as "A new improved and less expensive Steiff teddy bear." He was produced in white, blonde, and gold mohair in sizes ranging from 6in to 16in (15cm to 41cm). A smiling mouth is characteristic of *Dicky*. It appears the gold version's nose was stitched with black thread and the white and blonde version with brown thread. They also came with plain or painted paw pads. CONDITION: Excellent. PRICE: $9,000–up. *Private Collection.*

Far left: *Dicky* Bear. Circa 1933. 18in (46cm); gold mohair; short gold mohair inset snout; painted velveteen paw pads (design on paw pads somewhat faded); glass eyes; f.j.; e.s.; FF button; remnants of red S.L. Rare. *Dicky* was produced in gold mohair from 1930 to 1936 and in white mohair from 1933 to 1934. In 1935, a dark brown wool plush *Dicky* was produced. CONDITION: Excellent. PRICE: $8,000–up. *Private Collection.*

Top right: Bear. Circa 1930. 20in (51cm); brown mohair; glass eyes; f.j.; e.s. CONDITION: Excellent. PRICE: $6,500–up. Steiff Rooster. Circa 1920. 7in (18cm); beige, yellow-gold and dark blue mohair; shoe-button eyes; n.j.; e.s. CONDITION: Excellent. PRICE: $800–up. Steiff Ball. Circa 1950. 10in (25cm); various colors of mohair; s.s. CONDITION: Excellent. PRICE: $100–$150. *Photograph Courtesy Horst Poestgens, Auctioneer, Germany.*

Above left: Bear. Circa 1930. 16in (41cm); dark brown mohair; glass eyes; f.j.; e.s. CONDITION: Fair. PRICE: $3,000–up. *Photograph Courtesy Horst Poestgens, Auctioneer, Germany.*

Above right: Bears. Circa 1930s. (Right) 16in (41cm) white mohair. (Left) 17in (43cm) golden mohair. Both bears have glass eyes; f.j.; e.s.; FF button. CONDITION: Excellent. PRICE: approximately $6,400 (Left), $4,000 (Right). Sold at Christie's South Kensington 1997 auction. *Courtesy Christie's.*

Right: Bear. Circa 1935. 28in (70cm); gold mohair; glass eyes; f.j.; e.s. CONDITION: Excellent. PRICE: $15,000–up. *Courtesy Puppenhausmuseum. Basel.*

Left: Circus Bear with Neck Mechanism. Circa 1936. 12in (30cm); brown mohair; short beige inset snout; glass eyes; snap jointed arms and legs; e.s.; mechanical head (head moves in circular motion when tail is turned). CONDITION: Excellent. PRICE: $6,000–$9,000. *Courtesy Puppenhausmuseum. Basel.*

Right: Bear. Circa 1948. 12in (31cm); dark brown synthetic silk plush; brushed flannel paw pads; glass eyes; f.j.; e.s.; blank button (probably the blue-painted button used only for a short period during World War II). During World War II, when mohair was expensive and scarce, Steiff used less expensive fabrics such as this synthetic silk plush. When the brushed flannel paw pads became worn, the material appears more woven. CONDITION: Excellent. PRICE: $2,500–up. *Private Collection.*

Top left: Bear with Neck Mechanism. Circa 1936. 9in (23cm); yellow mohair; short white mohair inset snout; glass eyes; n.j. legs; e.s. Head moves in circular motion when tail is turned. CONDITION: Fair. PRICE: $2,000–up. *Photograph Courtesy Horst Poestgens, Auctioneer, Germany*

Bottom left: Bear on All Fours. Circa 1930. 10in tall x 15in long (25cm x 38cm); cream-colored mohair; glass eyes; n.j.; e.s.; FF button; remnants of red S.L. CONDITION: Mint. PRICE: $2,000–up. *Private Collection.*

Top right: Bear with Neck Mechanism. Circa 1936. 12in (30cm) long; brown mohair; short beige mohair inset snout; glass eyes; n.j.; e.s.; FF button with trace of red label. Head moves in circular motion when tail is moved. CONDITION: Excellent. PRICE: $2,500–$3,500. *Private Collection.*

Bottom right; Bear (Left). Circa 1940. 11in (28cm); dense beige "wool" plush; "linen" paw pads; glass eyes; f.j.; e.s.; FF button. CONDITION: Excellent. PRICE: $2,400–up. Bear (Center). Circa 1940. 10in (25cm); gold "silk" plush; "linen" paw pads; shoe-button eyes; f.j.; e.s.; FF button. CONDITION: Excellent. PRICE: $2,400–up. Bear (Right). Circa 1925. 12in (31cm); white mohair; "linen" paw pads; glass eyes; f.j.; e.s. CONDITION: Excellent. PRICE: $2,000–up. Three examples of various materials Steiff used during the 1920's through 1940's. Note especially all bears have "linen" paw pads. Due to the increased costs of the mohair fabric during World War II, Steiff was forced to use the less expensive wool and silk plush for some of their toys. *Courtesy Patricia Volpe. Photograph by John Volpe.*

Far left: Bear. Circa 1940s. 20in (50cm); green/beige synthetic silk plush; glass eyes; brown stitched nose, mouth and claws; f.j.; e.s. CONDITION: Good. PRICE: $4,000–$5,000. *Courtesy Puppenhausmuseum. Basel.*

Top right: Bear. Circa 1948. 16in (40cm); yellow mohair; glass eyes; f.j.; e.s.; blank blue-painted button. "U.S. Zone Germany" tag under arm. Post war bear with pre-war pattern. CONDITION: Excellent. PRICE: $3,000–up. *Courtesy Puppenhausmuseum. Basel.*

Above left: *Schlenkerteddyli.* Circa 1946-1948. 10in (25cm); brown artificial silk head, paws and tops of feet; beige fabric body; felt-lined open mouth; glass eyes; f.j.; e.s.; R.S.B. CONDITION: Good. PRICE: $1,500–$2,000. *Courtesy Puppenhausmuseum. Basel.*

Above right: *Teddy.* 1947. 4in (10cm); beige mohair; glass eyes; f.j.; e.s.; FF button. Produced to commemorate Margarete Steiff's 100th birthday (July 24, 1847). CONDITION: Mint. PRICE: $5,000–up. *Courtesy David Douglass.*

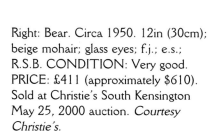

Teddy Bears
1950-1979

Right: Riding Bear. Circa 1950. 23in (58cm); brown mohair; short beige inset mohair snout; glass eyes; n.j.; e.s.; FF button; leather collar; pull growler; red painted metal wheels with rubber tires; metal frame. CONDITION: Excellent. PRICE: $1,500-$1,800. Not pictured:
Riding Bear. Circa 1967. R.S.B.
PRICE: 17in (43cm) $300–$400
        20in (50cm); $450–$550
        24in (60cm) $650–up

Left: *Teddy Babies*. (Left) Circa 1950. 8-½in (23cm); (Center) Circa 1930. 15-½in (40cm); long brown mohair; short beige mohair inset snout; beige felt-lined open mouth; short beige mohair tops of feet; f.j.; e.s.; red collar and bell. (Right) Steiff Rabbit. Circa 1920. 6-½in (17cm); blonde mohair; glass eyes; n.j. legs; swivel head; e.s.; FF button. CONDITION: **Teddy Babies**—Mint. Rabbit—Good. PRICE: **Teddy Baby** 8-½in (23cm) approximately $1,745; *Teddy Baby* 15-½in (40cm) approximately $1,850; Rabbit 6-½in (17cm) approximately $175. Sold at Horst Poestgens 1999 auction, Germany. *Courtesy Horst Poestgens, Auctioneer, Germany.*

Right: Bear. Circa 1950. 12in (30cm); beige mohair; glass eyes; f.j.; e.s.; R.S.B. CONDITION: Very good. PRICE: £411 (approximately $610). Sold at Christie's South Kensington May 25, 2000 auction. *Courtesy Christie's.*

Right: This group of miniature Steiff bears depicts the changes in Steiff's miniature bear designs from 1905 to 1960. All examples are approximately 3-½in (9cm); tall; shades of honey-colored mohair (with the exception of the center bear which is the rare white mohair); tiny black button eyes; f.j.; e.s. Note how the length of the mohair and shape of the faces change over the years. Prices indicated are for bears with Steiff buttons. CONDITION: Excellent.

PRICE: (Left) Circa 1910 $900–up
       (Second left) Circa 1925 $700–up
       (Center [white]) Circa 1940 $800–up
       (Second right) Circa 1952 $400–up
       (Right) Circa 1960 $300–up
Private Collection.

Left: Original Teddy. Circa 1950. Golden mohair; glass eyes; f.j.; e.s.; R.S.B.; C.T. CONDITION: Mint.
PRICE: 3-½in (9cm) $400–up
       10in (25cm) $525–up
       16in (41cm) $1,000–up
       26in (66cm) $4,500–up
       30in (76cm) $5,500–up
Rare colors command higher prices.

Right: *Teddy Baby* Musical Bear (Left). Circa 1948. 9in (23cm); head and arms dark brown mohair; short beige mohair inset snout; beige linen cloth body; glass eyes; n.j. arms; swivel head; e.s.; tube body conceals music box; R.S.B.; remnant of U.S. Zone label. Bellows produces music when tube body is pressed in downward motion. Music box (tube) marked "Thorens, Switzerland". CONDITION: Excellent. PRICE: $2,000–up. Musical Bear (Right). Circa 1952. 14in (36cm); beige mohair; glass eyes; f.j.; e.s.; music box concealed in tummy. Bellows produces music when tummy is squeezed. CONDITION: Good. PRICE: $3,000–up. *Courtesy Patricia Volpe, photograph by John Volpe.*

Right: *Original Teddy*. Circa 1950. 26in (66cm); golden mohair; glass eyes; f.j.; e.s.; R.S.B.; C.T. CONDITION: Excellent. PRICE: $5,000–up. *Courtesy Barbara Baldwin.*

Left: Musical Bear. Circa 1950. 13-¾in (35cm); caramel mohair; glass eyes; f.j.; e.s.; squeeze type musical mechanism encased in body. CONDITION: Excellent. PRICE: $3,500–$4,500. *Courtesy Puppenhausmuseum. Basel.*

Right: Teddy Doll (Left). Circa 1945. 8in (20cm); beige wool plush head; hands and feet; linen body; glass eyes; felt-lined open mouth; stationary arms and legs; swivel head; e.s. Red felt jacket; white linen shirt; dark blue felt trousers. CONDITION: Excellent. PRICE: $1,800–up. **Nimrod** Bear (Right). Circa 1954. 8in (20cm); honey-colored mohair; glass eyes; f.j.; e.s.; R.S.B.; yellow S.L.; C.T. Original hunting outfit, green felt shirt; orange felt hat; brown leather boots and gun. CONDITION: Mint. PRICE: $2,200–up. *Courtesy Patricia Volpe. Photograph John Volpe.*

Left: **Teddyli** (Girl) Bear. Circa 1950s. 9in (23cm); brown mohair; beige inset snout; cloth body; glass eyes; felt-lined open mouth; jointed arms; stationary legs; swivel head; R.S.B. Felt jacket and skirt; cotton shirt; cloth tag sewn into side seam reads: "U.S. Zone Germany". CONDITION: Excellent. PRICE: $1,500–$2,000. *Courtesy Puppenhausmuseum. Basel.*

Right: **Teddyli** (Boy) Bear. Circa 1950s. 9in (22cm); brown mohair; short beige mohair inset snout; felt-lined open mouth; cloth body; jointed arms; stationary legs; swivel head; R.S.B. Felt jacket and pants; cotton shirt; cloth tag sewn into side seam reads: "Made in U.S. Zone". CONDITION: Excellent. PRICE: $1,500–$2,000. *Courtesy Puppenhausmuseum. Basel.*

Left: **Teddy Baby** Hand puppet. Bear. Circa 1950s. 9in (22cm); brown mohair; short beige mohair inset snout; glass eyes; felt-lined open mouth; n.j.; e.s. head. CONDITION: Good. PRICE: $100–$125. *Courtesy Puppenhausmuseum. Basel.*

Right: *Teddy Baby* (Left). Circa 1950.
3-1/2 in (9cm); brown mohair; beige
velvet inset snout; f.j.; e.s. CONDITION:
Excellent. PRICE: $1,000–up. *Teddyli*
(Right). 4in (10cm); brown mohair; beige
inset snout; rubber body; n.j.; arms and
legs; swivel head; e.s.; R.S.B. CONDI-
TION: Excellent. PRICE: $1,200–up.

Left: *Zotty* Bears. Circa 1950. Long silky mohair; short mohair inset
snout; gold mohair chest; glass eyes; pink felt-lined open mouth; f.j.; e.s.;
paws turned in downward position; R.S.B.; C.T.

	Mint Condition	Good Condition	Worn Condition
9in (23cm	$275–up	$175–up	$100–up
14in (36cm)	$450–up	$300–up	$150–up
20in (51cm)	$650–up	$400–up	$200–up

Note: The majority of *Zotty* bears are produced in the caramel-colored
mohair tipped with white. Rare colors command higher prices.
Photograph courtesy Barbara Baldwin.

Right: *Zotty* Bear. Circa 1950. 14in (36cm); long silky white
mohair with gold mohair chest; glass eyes; dark brown thread
nose and claws; f.j.; s.s.; R.S.B. Rare color. CONDITION:
Mint. PRICE: $2,800–up. *Courtesy Barbara Baldwin.*

Left: *Zotty* Bear. Circa 1950. Approximately 10in (25cm); long wavy white mohair; glass eyes; beige felt-lined open mouth; f.j.; e.s.; R.S.B.; C.T. *Clownie*. Circa 1954. Approximately 8in (20cm); hand-painted rubber face; felt body and clothes; f.j.; e.s.; R.S.B.; C.T. *Nelly* Snail. Circa 1961. 7-¾in (17cm) long; velveteen and leather; black glass eyes; n.j.; e.s.; R.S.B. CONDITION: Mint.
PRICE: *Zotty* Bear $1,500–up
           Clownie $270–up
           Nellie Snail $240–up
Photograph courtesy Horst Poestgens, Auctioneer, Germany.

Right: *Panda*. (Left) Circa 1954. 10in (25cm); black and white mohair; glass eyes; f.j.; e.s.; R.S.B.; C.T. (Center) Steiff Original Teddy. Circa 1950. 16in (41cm); golden mohair; glass eyes; f.j.; e.s.; R.S.B.; C.T. *Zotty* Bear. (Right) Circa 1952. 10in (25cm); caramel mohair; short mohair inset snout; pink felt-lined open mouth; glass eyes; f.j.; e.s.; R.S.B.; C.T. CONDITION: Mint. PRICE: Panda, approximately $1,425; Original Teddy, approximately $1,000; *Zotty*, approximately $1,400. Sold at Horst Poestgens 1999 Auction, Germany. *Photograph courtesy Horst Poestgens, Auctioneer, Germany.*

Left: *Breuni-Bear* (for the Breuninger department store). Circa 1956. 5in (13cm); gold mohair head and legs; cloth body; glass eyes; n.j.; e.s.; R.S.B.; felt outfit; advertisement for department store Breuninger. CONDITION: Mint. PRICE: $1,500–$2,000. *Courtesy Puppenhausmuseum. Basel.*

Right: Original Teddy (movable head mechanism). 1955. 7in (18cm); beige mohair; glass eyes; jointed arms and legs; neck mechanism (head moves in circular motion when tail is turned; e.s. CONDITION: Excellent. PRICE: $1,800—up. *Courtesy Puppenhausmuseum. Basel.*

Left: Koala. Circa 1950. Pale gold mohair; short mohair face; glass eyes; gray felt nose; f.j.; e.s.; R.S.B.
CONDITION: Excellent.

PRICE:		
5in (13cm)	$300—up	
8in (20cm)	$450—up	
12in (31cm)	$650—up	

Right: Pandas. Circa 1950. 6in (15cm); 8-½in (22cm) 13-½in (34cm); and 20in (51cm); black and white mohair; glass eyes; f.j.; e.s.; R.S.B. Pandas are among the most interesting and rare animals in the world. It was Ruth Harkness who turned America into a panda-loving nation when she brought Su-Lin to Chicago's Brookfield Zoo in 1938. Toy makers foreseeing an opportunity quickly began to infiltrate the toy industry with adorable Pandas. Steiff introduced their first Panda design in 1938. A continuing demand allowed Steiff to include this appealing animal in their program into the 1960s. These friendly-looking creatures with their striking black and white fur make an attractive addition to any collection.
CONDITION: Mint

PRICE:		
6in (15cm)	$750—up	
8-½in (22cm)	$800—up	
13-½in (34cm)	$1,200—up	
20in (51cm)	$2,000—up	

Courtesy Dayle Rushall.

Right: Polar Bear. (Left) Circa 1950. 5-½in (14cm) tall; white mohair; glass eyes; n.j.; e.s. CONDITION: Excellent. PRICE: $250–$300. Young Bear. (Center) Circa 1950. 6-½in (17cm) tall; beige mohair; glass eyes; n.j.; e.s. CONDITION: Excellent. PRICE: $300–$350. Young Bear. (Right) Circa 1950. 5in (13cm) tall; beige mohair; glass eyes; n.j. legs; swivel head; e.s.; R.S.B. CONDITION: Excellent. PRICE: $200–$250.

Left: *Jackie*. Bear. Circa 1953. (Left) 7in (18cm); (Center) 10in (25cm); (Right) 14in (36cm); blonde mohair; glass eyes; f.j.; e.s.; R.S.B. Created as Steiff's first jubilee bear. Identifying features are dark shaded area for navel, pink silk thread horizontally stitched across nose. Note: The short chunky body is uncharacteristic of Steiff's classic teddy bear design. Produced between 1953 and 1955.
CONDITION: Mint
PRICE: 7in (18cm) $2,000–up
       10in (25cm) $1,500–up
       14in (36cm) $2,000–up
Private Collection.

Right: *Floppy* Panda. Circa 1950. 13in (33cm); black and white mohair; black felt eye lids; pinkish beige felt-lined open mouth; n.j.; e.s.; R.S.B. CONDITION: Good. PRICE: $200–$300. Bendy Panda. Circa 1960. 3in (8cm); black and white mohair; black bead eyes; n.j.; bendable limbs; e.s. CONDITION: Good. PRICE: $100–$150.
Courtesy Deborah and Donald Ratliff.

Top: Pandas. (Left to right) Circa 1950. 15in (38cm); 11in (28cm); 8-½in (22cm) 5-½in (14cm); black and white mohair; airbrushed facial features; beige felt-lined open mouth; gray leather-type paw pads; glass eyes; f.j.; e.s. R.S.B. CONDITION: Excellent. PRICE: $900–$2,000 (each). *Crabby* Lobster. Circa 1963. 4in (10cm); orange felt airbrushed body features; glass eyes; n.j.; e.s. R.S.B.; C.T. CONDITION: Mint. PRICE: $300–$400. Steiff V.W. Transporter. Circa 1960. 8-½in (21cm) long. CONDITION: Excellent. PRICE: $200–$300. *Photograph courtesy Horst Poestgens, Auctioneer, Germany.*

Bottom: Riding Bear. Circa 1960. Dark brown plush with short beige mohair inset snout; glass eyes; n.j.; e.s.; R.S.B.; detachable wooden rockers; disc wheels (painted red); white rubber tires. Wooden rockers were sold separately as an accessory for riding animals. CONDITION: Excellent. PRICE: $1,000–up. *Courtesy Brigitte Nohrudi*

Left: *Zooby* Bear. 11in (28cm); Circa 1964; brown mohair; beige mohair inset snout; dark brown mohair feet; open felt-lined mouth; plastic eyes; felt claws; jointed head and arms; stationary legs; R.S.B. CONDITION: Mint. PRICE: $1,000–$1,500.

Original Teddy Bear. Circa 1970. Caramel-colored mohair; short mohair heart-shaped face; glass eyes; synthetic pads; f.j.; e.s.; I.S.B.; C.T.
CONDITION: Excellent
PRICE:

10in (25cm)	$75–up
16in (41cm)	$125–up
26in (66cm)	$250–up
30in (76cm)	$475–up

Rare colors (such as the cream-colored bear pictured) command higher prices.

Left: Original Teddy Bears. (Front) Circa 1980. 9in (23cm); dark caramel mohair; short caramel mohair snout; plastic eyes; f.j.; s.s.; B.B. (Back) 1970; 19in (48cm); pale blond mohair; short blond mohair shield-shaped inset snout; glass eyes; f.j.; e.s. (firm) R.S.B. CONDITION: Excellent. PRICE: 9in (23cm) $75–$100. 19in (48cm) $200–up. *Courtesy Emma Stephens.*

@nimals
1890-1980

Since Margarete Steiff created a toy elephant in 1880, this fascinating animal's popularity has continued to grow in the Steiff range of toys. Over the years, the elephant has been included in a great number of their innovative designs. One of the most popular is the elephant mounted on wheels. Produced in many sizes, these impressive creatures came with metal and wooden wheels.

Elephants

Elephant on Wooden Wheels. (Left) Circa 1920. 8in (20cm). CONDITION: Good. PRICE: $500–up. Elephants on Cast Metal Wheels. Circa 1910. 10in–20in (25cm–51cm); gray felt; white padded felt tusks; shoe-button eyes; n.j.; e.s.; <u>FF</u> button; original felt blankets. CONDITION: Excellent. PRICE: $1,200–$2,000. *Courtesy Carolyn Wiggins.*

Right: Rod Elephant. Circa 1904. 10in x 12in (25cm x 31cm); gray nappy wool; shoe-button eyes; f.j.; metal rods connecting joints; e.s.; molded body; body extremely hard. Rare. CONDITION: Mint. PRICE: $3,000–up. *Courtesy Barbara Lauver.*

Left: Elephant on Wooden Wheels. Circa 1926. 14in x 11in (36cm x 28cm); charcoal gray mohair; white felt tusks; blue glass eyes; n.j.; e.s.; <u>FF</u> button. Metal frame with red painted wooden wheels. Original blue mohair blanket and headdress trimmed in red fringe. Produced from 1926 to 1928. CONDITION: Excellent. PRICE: $2,500–up. *Private collection.*

Right: Elephant. Circa 1930. 9in (23cm) tall; gray Persian lamb-like wool plush; shoe-button eyes cover round white felt circles; open gray-lined felt mouth; gray linen foot pads; n.j.; e.s.; embroidered red felt saddlecloth blanket. CONDITION: Worn. PRICE: $900–up. *Photograph courtesy Horst Poestgens, Auctioneer, Germany.*

Right: Elephant Doll (Left). Circa 1935. 11in (28cm); short gray mohair head and paws; cotton fabric body; blue glass eyes; n.j.; arms and legs; swivel head; e.s.; <u>FF</u> button; original clothes. CONDITION: Excellent. PRICE: $1,800—up. Elephant (Right). Circa 1910. Gray mohair; shoe-button eyes; f.j.; e.s.; <u>FF</u> button. CONDITION: Good. PRICE: $1,000—up. *Courtesy David Douglass.*

Left: Dangly Elephant. Circa 1950. 14in (36cm); short gray mohair; glass eyes; beige felt-lined open mouth; n.j. arms and legs; swivel head; e.s.; R.S.B. CONDITION: Excellent. PRICE: $800—up. *Courtesy David Douglass.*

Right: Riding Elephant. Circa 1950. 20in (51cm) tall; gray mohair; glass eyes; n.j.; e.s.; R.S.B.; disc wheels (painted blue); white rubber tires; mounted on metal frame. CONDITION: Excellent. PRICE: $1,200—up. *Courtesy Brigitte Nohrudi.*

Rabbits

Left: Rabbit Pen Wipe (Left). Circa 1890. 3in (8cm); cream-colored velveteen; airbrush design in brown; red pearl cotton nose and mouth; glass eyes with painted backs; n.j.; k.s. firmly stuffed; green felt base with scalloped edge. Extremely rare. According to Jorg Junginger, this rabbit is pre-button. Approximately 20 different animals were made in the design. CONDITION: Excellent. PRICE: $2,000–up. Rabbit (Right). Circa 1928. 6in (15cm); cream-colored velveteen; red pearl cotton nose and mouth; glass eyes; n.j.; swivel head; k.s. Note oversized ears for body. CONDITION: Excellent. PRICE: $1,000–up. *Private collection.*

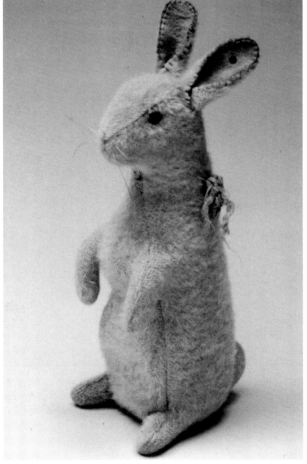

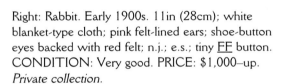

Right: Rabbit. Early 1900s. 11in (28cm); white blanket-type cloth; pink felt-lined ears; shoe-button eyes backed with red felt; n.j.; e.s.; tiny FF button. CONDITION: Very good. PRICE: $1,000–up. *Private collection.*

Left: Rabbit. Circa 1908. 9in x 4in (23cm x 10cm); black, white and gold mohair; white felt feet; shoe-button eyes backed with red felt; e.s.; n.j.; FF button; remnant of white tag. "Guinea Pig" type rabbit. CONDITION: Mint. PRICE: $900–up. *Private collection.*

Right: *Peter Rabbit* (Left). Circa 1908. 10in (25cm); cream-colored velveteen; airbrush design in brown; pink pearl cotton nose and mouth; shoe-button eyes backed with red felt; n.j.; tiny <u>FF</u> button. Dressed in a blue felt coat trimmed with gold braid and six brass buttons. Shoes are red felt with leather soles. Representing Beatrix Potter's famous *Peter Rabbit* storybook character. CONDITION: Excellent. PRICE: $2,500—up. *Jack Rabbit* (Right). Circa 1926. 13-½in (34cm); cream-tipped dark brown mohair head and paws; cream-colored mohair in center of forehead; ears are lined with pink velveteen; pink pearl cotton nose outlined with black thread; black pearl cotton mouth with red felt tongue; glass eyes; jointed arms and legs; stationary head; e.s.; <u>FF</u> button. Rare. Produced between 1927 and 1931 in sizes 9in (23cm); 11in (28cm). Velveteen clothes are not removable. Shoes are brown leather. CONDITION: Mint. PRICE: $4,000—up. *Private collection.*

Left: Rabbit (movable head mechanism) (Left). Circa 1950. 6in (15cm); off-white and white mohair; glass eyes; n.j.; neck mechanism (head moves in circular motion when tail is turned); e.s.; R.S.B. CONDITION: Very good. PRICE: $750—up. *Holland* Rabbit (Right). Circa 1908. 10in (25cm); white mohair; pink glass eyes; jointed arms, legs, "ears"; swivel head; e.s.; <u>FF</u> button. CONDITION: Excellent. PRICE: $1,500—up.

Right: Hare Family. Rattles. Circa 1910. Parents 5in (13cm) long; two sitting hares 3in (8cm) long; two hares on their haunches 5in (13cm) tall. Rattle encased in body of each hare. CONDITION: Good. PRICE: $5,000—up (set). *Photograph courtesy Horst Poestgens, Auctioneer, Germany.*

Top left: Velvet Rabbits. 1910–1929. 2-¼in–6in (6cm–15cm); velvet; glass eyes; n.j.; e.s.; FF button. CONDITION: Excellent. PRICE: $1,000–up (each). *Courtesy David Douglass.*

Bottom left: Rabbits with "Eccentric Wheels." Circa 1912. 7in (18cm), 9in (23cm), 12in (31cm), and 15in (38cm) long; tan felt; shoe-button eyes backed with red felt; n.j.; e.s.; wooden wheels stamped STEIFF. The largest rabbit wears a rose-colored ribbon with STEIFF printed on ribbon. The three smallest rabbits have weights in ears. The eccentric wheels give the animals a more natural movement and gait. CONDITION: Excellent. PRICE: 7in–15in (18cm–38cm) $950–$1,800. *Private collection.*

Top right: Clothes Brush. Circa 1914. 7-¾in x 3-½in (20cm x 9cm); cream-colored velveteen; airbrush design in brown; red pearl cotton nose and mouth; glass eyes (color painted on back); n.j.; k.s.; firmly stuffed. Rare. Steiff bristle brush also produced in the form of a clothes brush were a pig, a rabbit, and a dachshund. CONDITION: Excellent. PRICE: $1,200–up. *Private collection.*

Bottom right: Rabbits. Circa 1915. 5-¾in (14cm) and 6-¾in (17cm); beige felt; glass eyes; n.j.; e.s.; FF button. CONDITION: Excellent. PRICE: $1,500 (each). *Courtesy David Douglass.*

Top left: Hare. Circa 1920. 16in (41cm); white with brown-tipped mohair; glass eyes; n.j. arms and legs; swivel head; e.s. FF button. Steiff Wooly Chick. Circa 1935. FF button; red label. Steiff Egg Warmer. Rooster. Circa 1912. 6in (15cm); red and gold felt; shoe-button eyes; FF button. Steiff Egg Warmer. Chicken. Circa 1912. 4in (10cm); red and white felt; shoe-button eyes; FF button. CONDITION: Mint
Sold at Horst Poestgens 1999 Auction, Germany for approximately:

Hare	$1,000
Wooly Chick	$225
Rooster	$280
Chicken	$150

Courtesy Horst Poestgens, Auctioneer, Germany.

Bottom left: Roly-Droly Rabbits. Circa 1926. 5in (13cm); beige-tipped with brown mohair; shoe-button eyes; n.j. body; swivel head; e.s. FF button affixed to knob. Rabbits are attached to red wooden circles. When wooden wheeled frame is pulled, rabbits turn in circular motion. Rare. CONDITION: Mint. PRICE: $4,500–up. *Private collection.*

Top right: Rabbits (seated). Circa 1930. 2-½in (6cm); and 7in (18cm); various shades of beige and off-white mohair; glass eyes; n.j. legs; swivel head (except smallest rabbit); FF button; remnants of red S.T. CONDITION: Excellent. PRICE: 2-½ in (6 cm) $325; 7in (18cm) $400 (each).

Bottom right: Running Rabbit on Eccentric Wheels. Circa 1930. 12in (31cm); short blonde mohair; pink pearl cotton stitched nose outlined in black cotton; glass eyes; e.s.; red painted wooden wheels on metal frame. Eccentric wheels give the animal more natural movement and gait. CONDITION: Excellent. PRICE: $1,500–up. *Private collection.*

Far left: Rabbit (moveable head mechanism) (Left). Circa 1930. 4-¾in (12cm); light beige mohair; black-tipped ears; glass eyes; n.j. arms and legs; head moves by turning tail; e.s.; FF button; red label. Steiff advertised, "The ingenious head movement makes Steiff animals appear alive." The designer was Hugo Steiff. A label attached to the animal's tail read, "Turn here and I will move my head." CONDITION: Mint. PRICE: $1,500–up. Steiff Rabbit Rattle (Right). Circa 1920. 7in (18cm); orange mohair body; white chest and inner ears; glass eyes; stationary arms and legs; swivel head; e.s. Rare. Rattle is encased in stomach. CONDITION: Mint. PRICE: $1,800–up. *Private collection.*

Top right: Rabbit Doll Boy/Girl. Circa 1940. 9in (23cm); white mohair head, paws and feet airbrushed in brown; beige felt-lined ears; fabric bodies; glass eyes; e.s.; R.S.B.; original clothes. CONDITION: Excellent. PRICE: $1,800–up (pair). *Courtesy Barbara Baldwin.*

Above left: Rabbit. 1935. 8in (20cm); white and brown-tipped white mohair; glass eyes; f.j.; e.s.; FF button. CONDITION: Excellent. PRICE: $800. *Private collection.*

Above right: Rabbits. Circa 1933. (Left) 10-½in (26cm); (Right) 8-½-in (21cm); white mohair head, paws and feet; cotton fabric body; red pearl cotton stitched nose and mouth; glass eyes; n.j. arms and legs; swivel head; e.s.; FF button. Original blue and white cotton pajamas. CONDITION: Excellent. PRICE: (Left) $2,500–up (Right) $1,800–up. *Courtesy David Douglass.*

Right: *Niki*. Rabbits. Circa 1950. Mohair; glass eyes; f.j;
e.s.; R.S.B.; C.T. CONDITION: Mint to excellent.
PRICE:

Niki	5-½in (14cm)	$225–up
	6-½in (17cm)	$275–up
	8-½in (22cm)	$300–up
	11in (28cm)	$350–up
	13-¾in (35cm)	$500–up
Not pictured		
Floppy Hansi	6-½in (17cm)	$50–up
	11in (28cm)	$75–up
Sonny	3in (8cm)	$125–up
	6in (15cm)	$150–up
	7in (18cm)	$200–up
Hoppy	3in (8cm)	$65–up
	5in (14cm)	$95–up
	6-¾in (17cm)	$125–up
Pummy	6in (15cm)	$95–up
	10in (25cm)	$175–up
Lulac	17in (43cm)	$450–up
	23-¾in (60cm)	$750–up
Ossi	7in (18cm)	$150–up
	9in (23cm)	$175–up

Above: *Manni* Rabbit (Left). Circa 1960.
White/tan airbrushed mohair; glass eyes; n.j.
legs; swivel head; e.s.; R.S.B.
CONDITION: Mint to excellent.

PRICE:	4in (10cm)	$125–up
	8in (20cm)	$250–up
	11-¾in (30cm);	$400–up
	15-¾in (40cm)	$500–up
	21-¾in (55cm)	$750–up

Lying Rabbit (Right). Circa 1953. White
airbrushed mohair; glass eyes; n.j. legs; swivel
head; e.s.; R.S.B.
CONDITION: Mint to excellent.

PRICE:	2-½in (6cm)	$100–up
	3-½in (9cm)	$125–up
	4in (12cm)	$140–up

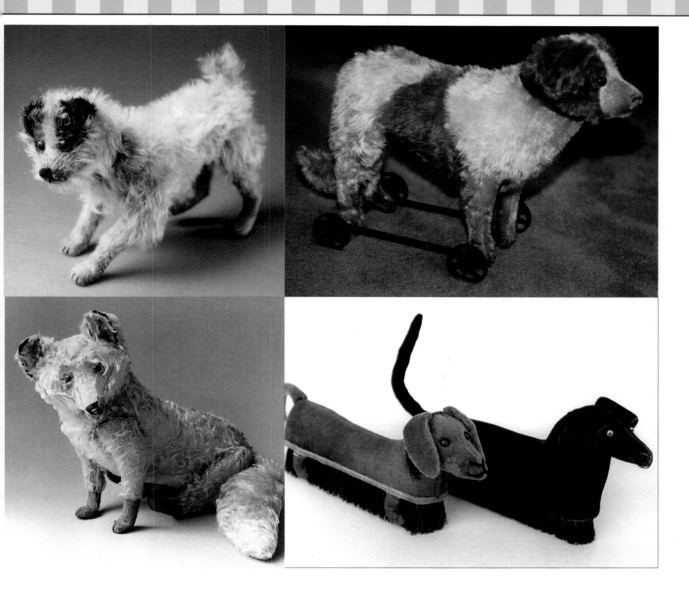

Top left: *Caesar* Terrier. Circa 1912. 8in (20cm); black/white mohair; glass eyes; f.j.; legs; swivel head; e.s.; FF button. *Caesar* was the favorite dog of British King, Edward VII. CONDITION: Excellent. PRICE: $1,200–up. *Courtesy David Douglas.*

Bottom left: Fox. Circa 1914. 20in (51cm) long; tan and white mohair; glass eyes; f.j.; e.s.; FF button. CONDITION: Excellent. PRICE: $1,000–up. *Courtesy David Douglass.*

Top right: Saint Bernard Dog on Metal Wheels. Circa 1913. 17in (43cm) tall; off-white and rust-colored mohair; brown pearl cotton stitched nose; glass eyes; n.j.; e.s.; original leather collar. CONDITION: Excellent. PRICE: $1,200–up. *Courtesy Barbara Baldwin.*

Bottom right: Clothes Brush. Dachshund. Dog. Circa 1914. 9in x 4in (23cm x 10cm); (left) brown velvet; shoe-button eyes. (right) black velvet; glass eyes; n.j.; e.s.; FF button; stiff bristle brush. CONDITION: Excellent. PRICE: $1,000–$1,200. *Courtesy Mimi Hiscox.*

Top left: Fox. Circa 1920. 17-¾in (45cm); gold/white mohair; glass eyes; f.j.; e.s.; purple-tipped white mohair hooded coat (skis not original). Part of a mechanical store display. CONDITION: Excellent. PRICE: $10,000–up. *Courtesy David Douglass.*

Bottom left: *Pip*. Circa 1928. 3in (8cm); orange velvet; beige velvet inset snout; glass googlie eyes; n.j. legs; swivel head; e.s.; FF button. C.T. CONDITION: Mint. PRICE: $850–up. *Courtesy David Douglas.*

Top right: *Charly* (King Charles Dog). Circa 1920. 7in (18cm); blonde and reddish-brown mohair; glass eyes; brown stitched nose, mouth and claws; stationary legs; swivel head; e.s.; FF button. CONDITION: Good. PRICE: $500–up. *Private collection.*

Bottom right: *Pip* Dog. Circa 1926. 5in (13cm); beige mohair tipped with brown (faded); large glass eyes; brown pearl cotton stitched nose, mouth and claws; small red felt tongue; n.j. arms and legs; swivel head; e.s.; FF button with red label. CONDITION: Good. PRICE: $550–up. *Courtesy David Douglass.*

Right: (Left to right) *Pip*. Circa 1928. 4in (10cm); brown velvet; googlie eyes; red felt tongue; n.j. legs; swivel head; e.s.; <u>FF</u> button (remains of red tag). The exaggerated Bulldog caricature *Pip* was inspired by A. B. Payne's comic from the British newspaper the *Daily Mirror,* "Pip, Squeak and Wilfred". *Chow Chow Brownie.* Circa 1930. 4in (10cm); golden beige mohair; glass eyes; n.j. legs; swivel head; e.s.; <u>FF</u> button. Reverse of chest tags reads, "Zeppelin Mascot". *Mollie* Dog. Circa 1930. 4in (10cm); bright green-tipped beige mohair; glass eyes; n.j. legs; swivel head; e.s.; <u>FF</u> button. CONDITION: Mint to excellent. PRICE: $500–$600 (each). *Courtesy Mimi Hiscox.*

Left: Representation of various rare *Bully* dogs. Circa 1928. (Left to right). *Bulliette*. 8in (20cm). CONDITION: Mint. PRICE: $1,500–up. *Bully*. 7in (18cm) (sitting). CONDITION: Mint. PRICE: $1,800–up. *Bully*. 4in (10cm) (standing). CONDITION: Mint. PRICE: $1,500–up. *Bully*. 3in (8cm) (sitting). CONDITION: Mint. PRICE: $1,200–up. *Courtesy David Douglas.*

Right: *Bulliette* (Top). Circa 1928. 8in (20cm); orange mohair; beige velvet head; beige mohair feet and paws; glass eyes; n.j. body; swivel head; e.s.; <u>FF</u> button. CONDITION: Mint. PRICE: $1,500–up. *Bully* on Wheels (Bottom). Circa 1928. 7in (18cm) tall; orange mohair/beige velvet head; beige mohair body; glass eyes; n.j. body; e.s.; <u>FF</u> button; mounted on wooden wheels CONDITION: Mint. PRICE: $1,800–up. *Courtesy David Douglas.*

Right: Dog (seated position). Circa 1925. 11in (28 cm); cream-colored mohair (originally was tipped brown); glass eyes; n.j. legs; stationary head; e.s.; FF button. CONDITION: Excellent. PRICE: $600–up. *Courtesy David Douglass.*

Left: *Bonzo* Dog. Circa 1927. 12in (31cm); beige velveteen; painted features; red felt tongue; glass googlie eyes; f.j.; e.s.; FF button; red S.L.; white C.T. Rare. CONDITION: Excellent. PRICE: $8,000–up. *Courtesy Barbara Baldwin.*

Right: *Bully.* Dog. Circa 1927. 8in (20cm); white and rust colored mohair; velvet muzzle; large glass eyes; n.j. legs; swivel head; wired ears; e.s.; FF button; remnants of red S.L.; horsehair ruff. *Bully* was produced sitting, standing, on wheels, ride-on-toy, eccentric wheels, a pull-toy, hand puppet, handbag and a pincushion. CONDITION: Excellent. PRICE: $1,500–up.

Top left: *Chow-Chow Brownie*, the Zeppelin mascot (seated). Circa 1928. 4in (10cm); bright cinnamon mohair; glass eyes; n.j. legs; swivel head; e.s.; FF button; C.T. CONDITION: Mint. PRICE: $700–up.

Bottom left: *Scotty* Dog (Left). Circa 1930. 3in (8cm); gray white-tipped mohair; glass eyes; n.j. legs; swivel head; e.s.; FF button; red S.L.; C.T. CONDITION: Excellent. PRICE: $500–up. *Treff* (Right). Circa 1928. 4in (10cm); beige mohair; glass eyes; FF button; red S.L.; C.T. *Treff* was adapted from the English Dalmatian *Dismal Desmond*. CONDITION: Mint. PRICE: $800–up.

Top right: *Cheerio* "The Laughing Puppy". Circa 1929. 7-½in (17cm); white/light brown mohair; large brown glass eyes; pink velvet smiling open mouth with tongue; n.j. legs; swivel head; FF button; red S.L. Unable to obtain licensing rights for *Bonzo*, Steiff created *Cheerio* as their portrayal. CONDITION: Excellent. PRICE: $1,500–up.

Bottom right: *Chin-Chin* the royal Chinese dog. Circa 1931. 5-½in (14cm); apricot-colored mohair; white mohair chest, face and feet; purple mohair inset snout; glass eyes; n.j. legs; swivel head; e.s.; FF button with red stock label; C.T.; original peach ribbon. CONDITION: Mint. PRICE: $1,000–up.

Right: *Fellow* Airedale Dog. Circa 1930. 7in (18cm); tan and black wavy mohair; glass eyes; n.j. legs; swivel head; e.s.; FF button; C.T. CONDITION: Mint. PRICE: $1,250–up. *Courtesy Barbara Baldwin.*

Left: Poodle Dog (movable head mechanism). Circa 1930. 13in (33cm); white mohair; shoe-button eyes; jointed arms and legs; mechanical head (head moves in circular motion when tail is moved). CONDITION: Excellent. PRICE: $2,000–up. *Courtesy David Douglass.*

Right: Animals (movable head mechanism). Head moves in circular motion by turning tail. Circa 1930. (Left to right) Rabbit. 6in (15cm); beige mohair; glass eyes; n.j. legs; e.s.; FF button. CONDITION: Good. PRICE: $900–$1,200. *Rattler* (the rat-catcher) Schnauzer Dogs. 4in/7in (10cm/18cm); brown-tipped blonde mohair; glass eyes; n.j. legs; e.s.; FF button; C.T.; tag on tail reads, "Turn here and I will move my head". CONDITION: Mint. PRICE: $1,200–$1,800. *Courtesy Mimi Hiscox.*

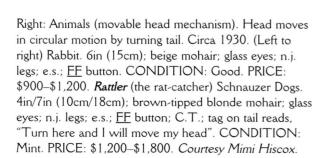

Far left: Fox Terrier (reclining). Circa 1933. 10in (25cm) tall; white wool plush; gray-brown ears; glass eyes; n.j.; e.s. CONDITION: Excellent. PRICE: $2,000–up. *Courtesy David Douglass.*

Top right: *Chow* Dog (Polar Spitz). Circa 1950. 6in (15cm) tall; white wool airbrushed with brown markings; glass eyes; n.j.; e.s.; R.S.B.; C.T. CONDITION: Mint. PRICE: $950–up. *Courtesy Barbara Baldwin.*

Above left: *Pug-Dog* (Left). Circa 1933. 11in (28cm); short blond, beige and brown mohair head; short blonde mohair arms and feet; cotton fabric body; glass eyes; n.j. arms and legs; swivel head; e.s.; FF button; red .S.L.; clothes not original. CONDITION: Good. PRICE: $650–up. *Treff* Dog Purse (Right). Circa 1931. 11in (28cm); short tan mohair; glass eyes; n.j. arms and legs; swivel head; e.s.; red S.L. The body of the dog is lined and the empty cavity serves as the purse. Pictured in Steiff's 1931 catalog only. CONDITION: Excellent. PRICE: $1,200–up. *Courtesy David Douglass.*

Above right: *Loopy* Wolf. Circa 1950. 12in (31cm); long and short gray silky mohair; short gray mohair inset snout; long red felt tongue; beige felt-lined mouth; glass eyes; stationary legs; swivel head; e.s.; R.S.B.; C.T. reads "Loopy". CONDITION: Mint. PRICE: $2,000–up. *Courtesy Barbara Baldwin.*

Far left: Dalmatian. Dog (begging position). Circa 1950. 5-½in (14cm); black and white mohair; black glass eyes; n.j. legs; swivel head; e.s.; R.S.B.; C.T.; sewn-on jeweled crown; red taffeta cape. Special issue for F.A.O. Schwarz. CONDITION: Mint. PRICE: $1,000–up. *Courtesy Barbara Baldwin.*

Top right: Sitting *Foxy*. Dog. Circa 1950. 6-½in (16cm) tall; white and tan mohair; glass eyes; n.j. legs; swivel head; e.s.; R.S.B.; C.T. Rare. CONDITION: Mint. PRICE: $750–$1,050. *Courtesy Barbara Baldwin.*

Above left: *Waldi.* (Dachshund dog mounted on wooden wheels). Circa 1950. 6-½in x 12in (16cm x 31cm); long beige mohair; short beige mohair face and legs; glass eyes; R.S.B.; C.T.; mounted on metal frame with red painted wooden wheels. CONDITION: Mint. PRICE: $750–up. *Courtesy Barbara Baldwin.*

Above right: *Bully* Dog (college mascot series) seated position. Circa 1950. 12in (31cm); short beige and brown mohair; large glass googlie eyes; n.j. legs; swivel head; e.s.; R.S.B.; U.S. Zone Germany label sewn into seam of body. CONDITION: Excellent. PRICE: $1,100–up. *Courtesy Barbara Baldwin.*

Right: *Bully* Dogs. Circa 1950. (Left to right)
5in–3-½in tall (13cm–9cm); short beige
mohair airbrushed in brown tones; beige
velvet airbrushed muzzle; glass eyes; n.j. legs;
swivel head; R.S.B.; C.T. Dogs are sewn onto
pillow and originally came in a wicker basket.
Made for F.A.O. Schwartz. CONDITION:
Mint. PRICE: $1,000-$1,200 (set). *Private
collection.*

Left: *Butch* Cocker (Left). Circa 1950.
6in (15cm); black and white mohair;
plastic googlie eyes; n.j. legs; swivel
head; e.s.; R.S.B. CONDITION:
Excellent. PRICE: $350. *Hexie*
Dachshund (Center). Circa 1955. 6in
(15cm); beige mohair airbrushed dark
brown; glass googlie eyes; n.j. legs;
swivel head; R.S.B.; C.T. CONDI-
TION: Mint. PRICE: $295. *Biggie*
Beagle (Right). Circa 1950. 7in (18cm);
white mohair air-brushed various
shades of brown; glass eyes; n.j. legs;
swivel head; R.S.B.; C.T. CONDI-
TION: Mint. PRICE: $225.

Right; *Molly* Dogs. Circa 1950. 4in (10cm) and 6in
(15cm); white mohair and dark brown-tipped
mohair; glass eyes; n.j.; R.S.B.; C.T. CONDI-
TION: Mint. PRICE: 4in (10cm) $200; 6in (15cm)
$275.

Top left: **Bazi** Musical Dog. Circa 1951. 9-½in (24cm); red-brown mohair head; short blonde mohair chin, body and arms; glass eyes; n.j. arms; swivel head; e.s.; R.S.B.; tube body conceals music box; bellows produces music when tube body is pressed in downward motion. Label sewn into side reads, "Made in U.S. Zone Germany." Originally wore clothes. CONDITION: Excellent. PRICE: $600–up. *Courtesy David Douglass.*

Bottom left: Bull Dog. 1998. 10in (25cm); white and brown mohair; plastic eyes; vinyl nose; n.j. legs; swivel head; s.s.; B.B.; C.T. CONDITION: Mint. PRICE: $150–up. *Private Collection.*

Top right: **Cosy Blanko** Dog. Circa 1970. 8in (20cm); white draylon; plastic eyes; n.j. legs; swivel head; s.s.; I.S.B.; C.T. CONDITION: Mint. PRICE: $150–up.

Bottom right: Olympic Doxie Bavarian Mascot. 1972. 10in x 14in (24cm x 36cm); lavender, turquoise and light green draylon and cotton; plastic eyes; n.j.; e.s.; I.S.B.; C.T. CONDITION: Mint. PRICE: $300-$325. *Courtesy Helen Sieverling.*

Left: Donkey on Wheels. Circa 1905. 9in (23cm) tall; light gray mohair over heavy fabric; shoe-button eyes; n.j.; e.s.; blank button; original leather saddle, harness and red felt blanket. CONDITION: Good. PRICE: $1,200–up. *Courtesy Barbara Baldwin.*

Right: Donkey on Wheels. Circa 1912. 9in (23cm); gray felt; shoe-button eyes; n.j.; e.s.; mounted on metal frame with green painted wooden wheels; original leather saddle and red felt blanket; FF button. CONDITION: Excellent. PRICE: $1,000–1,200. *Courtesy David Douglass.*

Left: Horse on Wheels. Pull toy. Circa 1908. 20in (51cm) tall; red-brown and beige felt; glass eyes; n.j.; e.s. FF button; black horse hair mane and tail; felt blanket; leather saddle; bridle and harness; metal wheels; frame and handle; handle crosses over horse to pull. CONDITION: Mint. PRICE: $4,300–up. Bear. Circa 1910. 13in (33cm); gold mohair; shoe-button eyes; f.j.; e.s.; FF button. CONDITION: Excellent. PRICE: $2,500–up. *Courtesy Barbara Baldwin.*

Right: Horse on Wooden Wheels (Left). Circa 1920. 10in (25cm); red-brown and cream-colored felt; glass eyes; n.j.; e.s. FF button; wooden wheels on metal frame; leather saddle. CONDITION: Excellent. PRICE: $750–up. Donkey on Metal Wheels (Right). Circa 1913. 8in (20cm); gray mohair; shoe-button eyes; n.j.; e.s.; FF button; metal wheels on metal frame; leather saddle. CONDITION: Excellent. PRICE: $850–up. *Courtesy David Douglass.*

Left: Sheep on Wheels. Circa 1912. 6in (15cm); off-white curly wool; light beige felt face, ears and legs; green glass eyes; red pearl cotton stitched nose and mouth; n.j.; green painted wooden wheels on metal frame; FF button. CONDITION: Excellent. PRICE: $900–up. *Courtesy David Douglass.*

Right: Sheep on Wheels. Circa 1938. 14in (36cm); off-white curly wool; short beige mohair inset snout, ears and base of legs; leather hooves; glass eyes; n.j.; e.s.; blue painted wooden wheels; FF button. CONDITION: Good. PRICE: $800–up. *Courtesy David Douglass.*

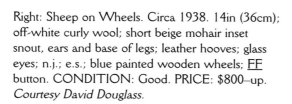

Top left: Goat. Circa 1928. 8in (20cm); white mohair; glass eyes; n.j. legs; swivel head; e.s.; FF button. CONDITION: Excellent. PRICE: $900–$1,000. *Courtesy David Douglass.*

Bottom left: Navy Goat. College Mascot Series (seated position). Circa 1949. 12in (31cm) long; short natural-colored mohair; leather hooves and horns; green googlie eyes; n.j.; e.s.; R.S.B.; C.T.; felt blanket. CONDITION: Mint. PRICE: $900–$1,000. *Courtesy Barbara Baldwin.*

Top right: **Lamby** (Left and center). Circa 1950. 4in (10cm) and 5-½in (12cm); off-white mohair; glass eyes; n.j.; e.s.; R.S.B.; C.T. CONDITION: Mint. PRICE: 4in (10cm) $125; 5-½in (12cm) $150–up. **Swapl.** Circa 1950. 5-½in (14cm); black wooly plush; blue glass eyes; n.j.; e.s.; R.S.B.; C.T. CONDITION: Mint. PRICE: $275–up.

Bottom right: (Left to right) Goat. Circa 1913. 16in (41cm); blonde mohair; green glass eyes; f.j.; e.s. CONDITION: Fair. PRICE: $650–up. Bear. Circa 1910. 10in (25cm); honey-colored mohair; shoe-button eyes; f.j.; e.s. CONDITION: Good. PRICE: $1,200–up. **Snik** Gnome. Circa 1913. 8in (20cm); beige felt face (painted features) and body; glass eyes; f.j.; e.s.; felt clothes. CONDITION: Excellent. PRICE: $1,200–up. *Courtesy Mimi Hiscox.*

Top left: Goats. Circa 1950. 4in (10cm) and 7in (18cm); off-white airbrushed mohair; glass eyes; n.j.; e.s. CONDITION: Excellent. PRICE: 4in (10cm) $125; 7in (18cm) $250.

Bottom left: (Left to right) Pig. Circa 1912. 4in (10cm) tall; pink velvet; small shoe-button eyes; red stitched nose and mouth; n.j.; e.s.; FF button. CONDITION: Excellent. PRICE: $750—up. Pig. Circa 1928. 6in (15cm) tall; white mohair; glass eyes; n.j.; e.s.; FF button; red S.L.; two-colored ruff. CONDITION: Excellent. PRICE: $1,200—up. Pig (movable head). Circa 1914. 6in (15cm) tall; blonde mohair; shoe-button eyes; jointed legs; ball-jointed neck; movable head (head moves in circular motion); e.s.; FF button. CONDITION: Excellent. PRICE: $1,200—up. *Courtesy David Douglass.*

Top right: Pig. Circa 1908. 8in x 12in (20cm x 31cm); shoe-button eyes; n.j.; e.s.; FF button; side squeaker. CONDITION: Excellent. PRICE: $1,250—$1,500. *Courtesy Barbara Baldwin.*

Bottom right: Guinea Pig. 1912. 5-1/2in (14cm); white, black and red mohair; shoe-button eyes; n.j.; e.s.; FF button. CONDITION: Excellent. PRICE: $1,500. *Courtesy David Douglass.*

Right: Goose. Circa 1910. 14in (36cm); white mohair; shoe-button eyes backed with red felt; orange felt beak and feet; f.j.; e.s. CONDITION: Good. PRICE: $600—up. *Courtesy David Douglass.*

Left: Family of Five Geese. Circa 1912. 7in–18in (18cm–46cm); white mohair; yellow felt beak and feet; n.j.; e.s.; <u>FF</u> button. CONDITION: Excellent. PRICE: $1,500–$2,500 (set). *Courtesy David Douglass.*

Right: Geese. Circa 1912. 8in, 12in, 14in (20cm, 31cm, 36cm); pale gold mohair; yellow felt beak and feet; shoe-button eyes; jointed legs; e.s. CONDITION: Excellent. PRICE: $700—up (each). *Courtesy David Douglass.*

Top left: Duck (movable head mechanism) (Left). Circa 1933. 8in (20cm); short green, gold and pale yellow mohair; orange felt beak and feet; black glass eyes; n.j. legs; e.s.; FF button. When tail is turned, head will move in circular motion. CONDITION: Excellent. PRICE: $850–up. Duck (Center). Circa 1926. 5in (13cm); short green gold and yellow mohair; orange felt beak and feet; black glass eyes; n.j.; e.s.; FF button. CONDITION: Excellent. PRICE: $400–up. Comic Duck (Right). Circa 1928. 6in (15cm); orange and faded yellow (originally blue) mohair; red felt beak and feet; black and white glass googlie eyes; n.j.; e.s.; FF button. CONDITION: Good. PRICE: $650–up. *Courtesy David Douglass.*

Bottom left: Duck on Eccentric Wheels. Circa 1920. 8in (20cm); various colors of felt feathers; gray felt body; green velvet head; orange felt beak and feet; shoe-button eyes; stationary head; e.s.; FF button; white S.L.; green painted wheels on metal frame; *STEIFF* marked on wheels; eccentric wheels give the animal a more natural movement and gait. CONDITION: Excellent. PRICE: $1,000–up. *Courtesy David Douglass.*

Top right: Duckling (Left). Circa 1938. 4in (10cm); blonde "wool" plush; orange felt beak and feet; black glass eyes; n.j.; e.s. FF button. CONDITION: Good. PRICE: $250–up. Duckling (Center left). Circa 1935. 6in (15cm); yellow "wool" plush; orange felt beak and feet; black glass eyes; n.j.; e.s. FF button. CONDITION: Good. PRICE: $350–up. Duck Doll (Center right). Circa 1933. 11in (28cm); pale yellow mohair, head, paws and feet; cotton fabric body; orange felt beak; shoe-button eyes; n.j. arms and legs; swivel head; e.s.; FF button; original bathing suit. CONDITION: Good. PRICE: $950–up. Duckling (Right). Circa 1935. 6in (15cm); white "wool" plush; orange felt beak and feet; black glass eyes; n.j.; e.s. CONDITION: Good. PRICE: $250–up. *Courtesy David Douglass.*

Bottom right; Chick (Left). Circa 1925. 3in (8cm); white mohair; yellow felt beak and feet; shoe-button eyes; n.j.; e.s.; FF button. CONDITION: Excellent. PRICE: $1,000–up. Hen Egg Warmers (Right). Circa 1912. 4in (10cm); white and red felt; FF button. CONDITION: Excellent. PRICE: $250–up (each). *Courtesy David Douglass.*

Right: Hen. Circa 1912. 11-¾in (30cm); pale gold mohair; brown mohair wings; dark gray mohair tail; red felt face; yellow felt feet; shoe-button eyes; n.j.; e.s.; FF button. CONDITION: Excellent. PRICE: $1,500. Chicks. Circa 1912. 3in (8cm); pale yellow mohair; shoe-button eyes; n.j.; e.s.; FF button. CONDITION: Excellent. PRICE: $1,000 (each). *Courtesy David Douglass.*

Left: Comic Hen. Circa 1928. 9in (23cm); pale, yellow, gold and green mohair; red felt face; shoe-button eyes backed with white felt; n.j.; e.s.; FF button. CONDITION: Excellent. PRICE: $850–up. *Courtesy David Douglass.*

Right: Rooster and Hen (Left and right). Circa 1950. 3in (8cm); mohair; felt head; glass eyes; metal feet; n.j.; R.S.B.; C.T. CONDITION: Mint. PRICE: $100 (each). Turkey (Center). Circa 1950. 4in (10cm); mohair; felt tail; glass eyes; metal feet; n.j. CONDITION: Excellent. PRICE: $175.

Top left: Lion on Wheels. Circa 1912. 8in (20cm); gold mohair; red pearl cotton stitched nose outlined in black; glass eyes; n.j.; e.s.; mounted on metal frame with metal wheels; <u>FF</u> button. CONDITION: Excellent. PRICE: $1,000–$1,200. *Courtesy David Douglass.*

Bottom left: Lion Pin Cushion. Circa 1914. 8in (20cm) long; gold velvet head and body; gold mohair mane; shoe-button eyes; n.j. legs; stationary head; e.s.; blank button; dark gold velvet pillow. CONDITION: Good. PRICE: $1,000–$1,200. *Courtesy David Douglass.*

Top right: Lion College Mascot Series. Circa 1948. 18in (46cm); gold mohair; long red-brown mohair mane; red pearl cotton stitched nose outlined in black cotton; glass googlie eyes; n.j.; e.s. Label sewn into seam of body reads: "U.S. Zone Germany". CONDITION: Excellent. PRICE: $1,000–up. *Courtesy David Douglass.*

Bottom right: Tiger. College Mascot Series (seated position). Circa 1950. 12in (31cm); beige mohair airbrushed in orange with black stripes; green glass googlie eyes; n.j. legs; swivel head; e.s.; R.S.B. CONDITION: Mint. PRICE: $1,500–up. *Courtesy Barbara Baldwin.*

Top left: Frog Pin Cushion. Circa 1905. 1-½in (4cm); green and beige velvet; shoe-button eyes; n.j.; e.s.; seated on green felt leaf. CONDITION: Excellent. PRICE: $2,000. *Courtesy David Douglass.*

Bottom left: Kangaroo. Circa 1912. 13-¾in (35cm); gray coat cloth; shoe-button eyes; f.j.; e.s.; FF button. CONDITION: Very good. PRICE: $1,200. *Courtesy David Douglass.*

Top right: Fawns. Circa 1930. (Left) 6-½in (17cm) (standing). (Right) 4-½in (12cm) (reclining); beige mohair; glass eyes; n.j.; e.s.; FF button. CONDITION: Excellent. PRICE: $400 (standing), $1,200 (reclining). *Courtesy David Douglass.*

Bottom right: Walt Disney's® ***Bambi*** (Left and Center). Circa 1952. 5-½in (14cm) and 8-½in (22cm); tan airbrushed velvet; off-white mohair chest; glass eyes; n.j.; e.s.; 5-½in (14cm) has R.S.B. and C.T. CONDITION: Mint. PRICE: 5 ½in (14cm) $200, 8-½in (22cm) $250. Fawn (Right). Circa 1950. 5in (13cm); tan airbrushed velvet; glass eyes; n.j.; e.s. CONDITION: Very good. PRICE: $125.

Right: Birds with Movable Wings. Circa 1958. 4-¼in (11cm); various colors of mohair; dyed horsehair wings; glass eyes; n.j.; e.s.; R.S.B.; yellow S.L.; C.T. Squeezing legs together activates wing movement. CONDITION: Mint. PRICE: $375–up (each). *Courtesy Barbara Baldwin.*

Left: Owl. Circa 1960; 31-¾in (80cm); white and brown mohair airbrushed with black and brown; large glass eyes; n.j. legs; swivel head; e.s.; R.S.B. CONDITION: Excellent. PRICE: $2,500–up. *Courtesy David Douglass.*

Right: Squirrels. Circa 1915. 8in–12in (3cm–31cm); mohair; shoe-button eyes; f.j.; e.s.; FF button. CONDITION: Mint. PRICE: $1,200–up (each). *Courtesy David Douglass.*

Right: Opossum (Left). Circa 1909. 12in (31cm) long; light honey-colored mohair tipped with brown; shoe-button eyes; f.j.; swivel tail; e.s.; FF button. Rare. CONDITION: Excellent. PRICE: $5,500–up. Pig (moveable head) (Right). Circa 1914. 5in (13cm) tall; white mohair; shoe-button eyes; jointed legs; ball-jointed neck; movable head (head moves in circular motion); e.s.; FF button; remnant white S.L. CONDITION: Excellent. PRICE: 1,500. *Private Collection.*

Left: Opossum. Circa 1909. 7in (18cm); white mohair; shoe-button eyes; red pearl cotton nose, mouth and claws; f.j.; e.s.; FF button. Rare size. CONDITION: Good. PRICE: $3,500–up. *Courtesy David Douglass.*

Right: Squirrel (Left). Circa 1920. 8in (20cm); red mohair; white mohair body front; glass eyes; f.j. (including tail); e.s. CONDITION: Excellent. PRICE: $1,200–$1,400. *Troll* Hunting Dog (Right). Circa 1930. 10in (25cm); cinnamon and pale beige mohair; glass eyes; n.j.; e.s. CONDITION: Excellent. PRICE: $1,500–$2,000. *Courtesy David Douglass.*

Right: (Top left to right) *Perri* Squirrel. Circa 1950. 3-½in (9cm); C.T. CONDITION: Mint. PRICE: $115. *Joggi* Hedgehog. Circa 1950. 5in (13cm); C.T. CONDITION: Mint. PRICE: $175. (Bottom left to right) *Raccy* Raccoon. Circa 1950. 6-½in (14cm); C.T. CONDITION: Mint. PRICE: $150. Dormouse. Circa 1960. 4in (10cm) long; C.T. CONDITION: Mint. PRICE: $115. *Maxi* Mole. Circa 1960. 4in (10cm); C.T. CONDITION: Mint. PRICE: $125. *Possy* Squirrel. Circa 1960. 5in (13cm); C.T. CONDITION: Mint. PRICE: $125. All animals have R.S.B.

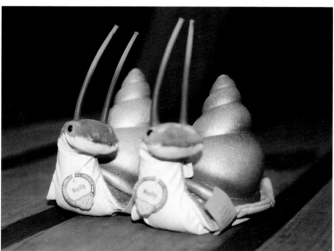

Left: *Nelly* Snails. Circa 1950. 4in (10cm); green and brown velvet; plastic shells and antennae; glass eyes; R.S.B.; yellow S.L.; C.T. CONDITION: Mint. PRICE: $450—up (each). *Courtesy Barbara Baldwin.*

Right: Texas Long Horned Steer. Circa 1962. 9in (23cm); short beige mohair; felt-lined open mouth; glass eyes; n.j.; e.s.; R.S.B. Rare. CONDITION: Very good. PRICE: $1,000—up. *Private collection.*

Top left: **Moosey Moose**. Circa 1950. 6in (15cm); short brown and beige mohair; beige felt antlers; glass eyes; n.j. legs; swivel head; e.s.; R.S.B.; C.T. CONDITION: Mint. PRICE: $600–$700. *Courtesy Barbara Baldwin.*

Bottom left: Hedgehogs. (Back left to right) **Micki, Mecki**. (Bottom left to right) **Mecki, Micki**. Circa 1950. 10in (25cm) and 8in (20cm); rubber faces; painted facial features; white-tipped brown hair; felt bodies; f.j.; e.s.; R.S.B. CONDITION: Excellent. PRICE: $125–$150 and up (each).

Top right: Hide-a-Gifts. Circa 1960. 6in (15cm); mohair heads and arms (except plush fox); plastic eyes; felt dresses (hollow underneath to hide small gift); R.S.B.; C.T. CONDITION: Mint. PRICE: $125–175 (each).

Bottom right: **Renny** Reindeer. Circa 1950. 7in (18cm) and 5in (13cm); white mohair airbrushed in various shades of brown; long white mohair ruff; felt covered wire antlers; glass eyes; n.j.; R.S.B.; C.T. CONDITION: Mint. PRICE: $200–$250. Santa Claus. Circa 1950. 5in (13cm); vinyl face and hands; mohair beard; red felt clothes with white plush trim; n.j. arms and legs; swivel head; C.T. CONDITION: Very good. PRICE: $250.

Top left: **Mickey Mouse**. Circa 1930. 20in (51cm); black/beige/gold velvet; n.j. arms and legs; swivel head; e.s.; FF button; foot stamp. Rare size. CONDITION: Mint. PRICE: $6,500–up. *Courtesy Barbara Baldwin.*

Bottom left: **Mickey Mouse** (Left). Circa 1931. 6-½in (16cm); black and white velvet, with black felt ears; applied "cherry pie" eyes; black velvet button nose; airbrushed facial features, yellow velvet glove hands, green velvet shorts and mother of pearl buttons, orange velvet card lined shoes stamped on base; FF button in ear with hint of red label. CONDITION: Good. PRICE: £977 (approximately $1,450). **Fox Terrier Dog** (Right). Circa 1920. 10in (25cm); cream mohair; black airbrushed right eye markings; orange mohair ears and tail; shoe-button eyes; f.j.; e.s.; FF button. CONDITION: Excellent. PRICE: £437 (approximately $650). Sold at Christie's South Kensington December 6, 1999 auction. *Courtesy Christie's.*

Top right: Markin 150th Texas Armadilla. 1994. 19in (48cm) (without tail); brown synthetic plush; plastic eyes; n.j.; s.s.; B.B.; C.T. CONDITION: Excellent. PRICE: $175–$225. *Private Collection.*

Bottom right: Advertising Rat. 1997. 14-½in (37cm); gray felt; black button eyes; n.j.; s.s.; B.B.; red jump suit with "Steiff", "Shell" and "Auda Air" label stitched on suit. Named after racecar driver Niki Lauder, made for Lauder-Air. CONDITION: Mint. PRICE: $200.

Top left: Steiff First Issue Jungle Book Characters. 1968–1974. Draylon; plastic eyes; felt and velour features; s.s. and e.s.; Walt Disney copyrights. CONDITION: Excellent. (Left to right) *Baloo.* 16in (41cm). PRICE: $1,000–up. *Baby Hathi.* 8in (20cm). PRICE $275–up. *King Louie.* 10in (25cm). PRICE: $375–up. *Shere Khan.* 14in (36cm). PRICE: $600–up. Value increases when sold as a set. *Private collection.*

Bottom left: Classic *Wind in the Willows* (Left to right). 1999. *Badger.* 11in (28cm). *Mr. Toad.* 10in (25cm). *Ratty.* 10in (25cm). *Mole.* 9-½ in (24cm). All animals mohair; plastic eyes; f.j.; s.s.; B.B.; white S.L. Limited edition 4,000 each. CONDITION: Mint. PRICE: *Badger* $325; *Mr. Toad* $325; *Ratty* $260; *Mole* $325. *Private collection.*

Top right: Steiff is renowned for creating animals with such realism they almost look alive. F.A.O. Schwarz exclusives. Baby Snow Leopard. 1991. White Tiger Cub. 1992. Florida Panther. 1994. *Courtesy Steiff.*

Bottom right: Warner Bros. Characters. (Left to right) *Tweety.* 1998. 8in (20cm). *Sly.* 1998. 13in (33cm). *Bugs.* 1997. 12in (31cm)(without ears). Frog. 1999. 13in (33cm)(without hat). Limited edition of 2,500 each. CONDITION: Mint. PRICE: *Tweety* $525; *Sly* $525; *Bugs* $335; Frog $295. *Private collection.*

Studio Pieces

Right: Animated Display. Circa 1950. 66in (167cm). Steiff *Micki* and *Mecki* and other Steiff animals come to life in an amusing setting, driven by electric motors.
CONDITION: Good.
PRICE: $7,000–up.

Below: Stagecoach. Circa 1950. 21in (53cm) tall; painted wood; pulled by two Steiff donkeys.
CONDITION: Excellent.
PRICE: $2,500–up. Steiff, Schuco and Hermann animals and dolls decorate the stagecoach. Circa 1950–1980. CONDITION: Excellent. PRICE: $150–$300 each.

Above: Studio Elephants. Circa 1950. Mohair; glass eyes; n.j.; e.s.; R.S.B. CONDITION: Excellent. Sizes are approximate. Elephant. 32in (81cm) tall. PRICE: $1,000–up. 33in (84cm) tall. PRICE: $1,200–up. 60in (152cm) tall. PRICE: $3,000–up.

Studio Animals not pictured:
Standing Bear. 66in (167cm) tall. PRICE: $3,000–up.
Polar Bear. 62in (157cm) tall. PRICE: $2,000–up.
Panda. 62in (157cm) tall. PRICE: $1,000–up.
Giraffe. 36in (91cm) tall. PRICE: $500–up; 60in (152cm) tall. PRICE: $1,200–up; 96in (243cm) tall. PRICE: $2,800–up.
Lion (sitting). 30in (76cm) tall. PRICE: $2,000–up.
Lion (standing). 40in (101cm) tall. PRICE: $2,000–up.
Tiger (standing). 40in (101cm) tall. PRICE: $2,000–up.
Chimpanzee. 60in (152cm) tall. PRICE: $1,000–up.
Pony. 39in (99cm) tall. PRICE: $1,200–up.
Reindeer. 48in (122cm) tall. PRICE: $2,500–up.
Camel. 40in (101cm) tall. PRICE: $2,500–up.
Collie Dog (laying). 48in 122cm) long. PRICE: $2,000–up.

Right: Studio Fox (Top). Circa 1950. 22in (56cm); white mohair/white mohair airbrushed with orange; felt open mouth and tongue; plastic teeth; glass eyes; n.j. legs; swivel head; e.s.; R.S.B. CONDITION: Mint. PRICE: $1,500–up. Lying Fox (Bottom). Circa 1965. 5in (13cm) tall; white/white airbrushed red wooly plush body; black mohair leg; n.j.; e.s. head; s.s. body; R.S.B.; C.T. CONDITION: Excellent. PRICE: $275.

Dolls

Right: *Coloro*. Circus Clown (Left). Circa 1905. 17in (43cm); bright green felt, face and body; green mohair hair; shoe-button eyes; f.j.; e.s.; velvet patterned outfit; FF button. CONDITION: Excellent. PRICE: $3,000–up. *Sailor* (Center). Circa 1905. 15in (38cm); navy felt sailor outfit (an integral part of body); beige felt face, torso and hands; red mohair beard; f.j. (with "metal rods"); e.s.; FF button. CONDITION: Excellent. PRICE: $4,500–up. *American Policeman* (Right). Circa 1905. 17in (43cm); beige felt face and hands; shoe-button eyes; navy felt policeman outfit (an integral part of body); beige felt hat; f.j. (with "metal rods"); e.s.; FF button. CONDITION: Excellent. PRICE: $3,500–up.

Left: *Golliwog*. Circa 1908. 11in (28cm); black felt head and hands; black mohair hair; shoe-button eyes backed with white and red felt circles; red and white stitched mouth; integral felt clothes; f.j.; e.s. Repaired patch on back. CONDITION: Very good. PRICE: $7,500–up. *Photograph courtesy Horst Poestgens, auctioneer, Germany.*

Right: *Happy Hooligan*. Circa 1910. 13-¾in (35cm); beige felt face; hand-painted facial features; shoe-button eyes; felt clothes an integral part of body; f.j.; e.s.; FF button. CONDITION: Excellent. PRICE: $3,000. *Courtesy David Douglass.*

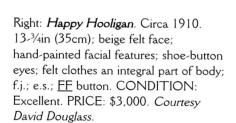

Left: *Mother Hubbard* (Witch). Circa 1910. 17in (43cm); beige felt face and hands; hand-painted facial features; grayish hair; blue felt top an integral part of body; separate fabric skirt; black felt hat; shoe-button eyes; f.j.; e.s.; FF button. CONDITION: Very good. PRICE: $2,500–up. *Courtesy David Douglass.*

Right: *Gaston*. 1912. 17-½in (45cm); beige felt face and hands; hand-painted features; shoe-button eyes; f.j.; e.s.; FF button; felt clothes an integral part of body. CONDITION: Excellent. PRICE: $2,500–up. *Courtesy David Douglass.*

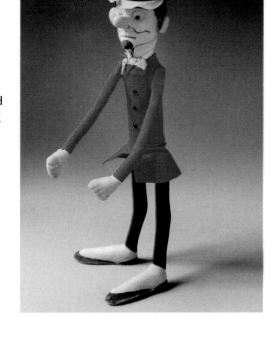

Left: *Mr. Twee Deedle*. Circa 1913. 13-¾in (35cm); beige felt face and hands; hand-painted facial features; shoe-button eyes; blonde hair; f.j.; e.s.; FF button. CONDITION: Excellent. PRICE: $3,000–up. *Courtesy David Douglass.*

Right: Sportsman. Circa 1914. 20in (51cm); beige felt face; hand-painted facial features; fabric body; original clothes; shoe-button eyes; f.j.; e.s.; <u>FF</u> button. CONDITION: Excellent. PRICE: $3,000. *Courtesy David Douglass.*

Left: ***Anton*** from Upper Bavaria. Doll. Circa 1910. 10in (25cm); felt face, body and clothes; shoe-button eyes; f.j.; e.s.; <u>FF</u> button. CONDITION: Mint. PRICE: $1,200–$1,500. *Courtesy Mimi Hiscox.*

Right: Lamb on Wheels (Left). Circa 1920. 14in tall x 15in long (36cm x 38cm); lambs wool and felt; red yarn nose and mouth; green glass eyes; n.j.; e.s.; metal frame; wooden wheels. CONDITION: Excellent. PRICE: $1,200–up. Dutch Doll (Right). Circa 1911. 17in (43cm); felt body; blue glass eyes; f.j.; e.s. CONDITION: Excellent. PRICE: $1,200–up. *Courtesy Lisa Vought.*

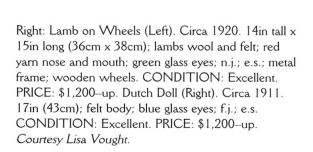

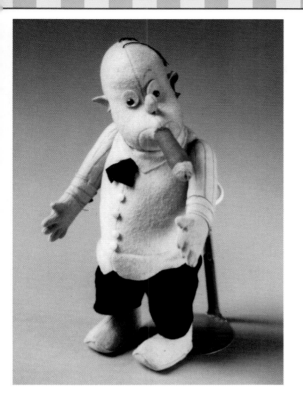

Right: *Adamson*. Doll. Circa 1925. 11in (28cm); beige cream and black felt (jacket an integral part of body); f.j.; e.s.; <u>FF</u> button; red stock label; cigar in mouth. Rare. CONDITION: Excellent. PRICE: $3,000–up. *Courtesy David Douglass.*

Left: *Dryboy*. Circa 1926. 7in (18cm); felt doll; red hair; purple felt jacket and green felt pants are integral part of body; shoe-button eyes; jointed body; swivel head; e.s. Doll rides wooden wheel tricycle. Rare. Only 480 pieces were produced. CONDITION: Excellent. PRICE: $5,000–up. *Private collection.*

Right: *Mat*. Clown Doll. Circa 1950. 8in (20cm); rubber face; felt body; n.j. legs; jointed arms; swivel head; e.s.; R.S.B.; C.T. CONDITION: Mint. PRICE: $450.

Chapter Three

Museum Replicas, Special and Limited Editions
1980-2001

In celebration of Steiff's 100th anniversary of making stuffed toys, a museum was opened in 1980 in the first Steiff factory building in Giengen, Germany. In the 1980s, Steiff introduced their Museum Series. Exact replicas of their rare and wonderful bears and animals became available for the avid Steiff collector.

Special Editions

Special editions are of the utmost interest to collectors because of their limited distribution and rarity, as well as the unique influence such partnerships add to the Steiff design. American editions predominate this particular book.

Right: Jubilee (Papa Bear) (Left). 1980. 17in (43cm); gold-colored mohair; black plastic eyes; f.j.; e.s.; B.B.; white woven S.L.; boxed with certificate. Limited edition of 11,000 pieces worldwide. Of this, 5,000 have an English certificate and were only sold in America. CONDITION: Mint. PRICE: $950. Mama and Baby set (Right). 1981. Mama 15in (38cm). Baby 6in (15cm); gold-colored mohair; black plastic eyes; f.j.; s.s.; B.B.; white woven S.L.; originally an orange ribbon encircled mother and baby with words "Margaret Steiff/KNOPF IMOHR/Ltd. Edition;" boxed with certificate. Limited edition of 8,000 pieces with an English certificate. Available only in America. CONDITION: Mint. PRICE: $600 (set).

Left: *Clifford Berryman Bear*® (Left). 1987. 13in (35cm); brown mohair; white mohair inset snout; felt-lined open mouth; airbrushed paw pads; black and white plastic googlie eyes; f.j.; s.s.; B.B.; yellow cloth-weave S.L. Discontinued. To commemorate renowned cartoonist Clifford Berryman's immortal portrayal of Teddy Roosevelt's 1902 bear hunt in Mississippi, Linda Mullins, together with the Steiff company, created the 85th Anniversary *Clifford Berryman Bear*®. CONDITION: Mint. PRICE: $400. *Richard Steiff* Bear (Right). 1983 (Replica 1905 design). 12in (32cm); gray mohair; black plastic eyes; f.j.; s.s.; B.B.; white S.L. boxed with certificate. Limited edition 20,000. CONDITION: Mint. PRICE: $550.

Left: *Ophelia* Bear. 1984. 16-½in (42cm); white mohair; plastic eyes; f.j.; s.s.; B.B. (issued button only); tab on leg; not issued with a box; U.S.A. only (ear tag #0225/42). *Photograph courtesy Steiff.* Please refer to page 127 for price guide.

Right: *Teddy Bear Replica 1909*. 1983. 11in (28cm), 15in (38cm), 20in (51cm); gold mohair; B.B.; yellow S.L. (ear tag #406331, #406379). *Photograph courtesy Steiff.* Please refer to page 125 for price guide.

Left: *Mr. Cinnamon* Bear. 1984 (Replica 1903 design). 10in (25cm); 12-½in (32cm); 15-¾in (40cm); cinnamon mohair; plastic eyes; f.j.; e.s.; B.B. yellow label (ear tag #0151/25, 0151/32, 0151/40). *Photograph courtesy Steiff.* Please refer to page 126 for price guide.

Right: *Margaret Strong* Cream Bears. 1984–1986 (Replica 1904 design). 10in (26cm); 13in (32cm); 16in (42cm); cream mohair; plastic eyes; f.j.; s.s.; B.B.; yellow label (ear tag #0157/26, 0157/32, 0157/42). *Photograph courtesy Steiff.* Please refer to page 126 for price guide.

Left: *Giengen Teddy Set* (Left). 1984. Mother 12-½in (32cm). Baby. 4in (10cm); white S.L.; limited edition 16,000 (ear tag #0162/00). *Teddy Bear Replica 1909 Gold* (Center). 1983. 15in (38cm); yellow S.L. (ear tag #0165/38). *Felt Elephant* (Right). 1984. (Replica 1880 design, Museum Collection). 3in (8cm); white S.L.; limited edition 10,000 (ear tag #0080/08). Replica of the first soft toy made by Margarete Steiff. *Photograph courtesy Steiff.* Please refer to pages 125–126 for price guide.

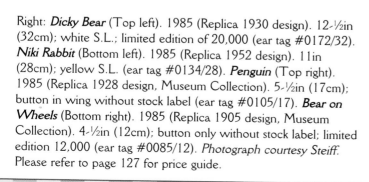

Right: *Dicky Bear* (Top left). 1985 (Replica 1930 design). 12-½in (32cm); white S.L.; limited edition of 20,000 (ear tag #0172/32). *Niki Rabbit* (Bottom left). 1985 (Replica 1952 design). 11in (28cm); yellow S.L. (ear tag #0134/28). *Penguin* (Top right). 1985 (Replica 1928 design, Museum Collection). 5-½in (17cm); button in wing without stock label (ear tag #0105/17). *Bear on Wheels* (Bottom right). 1985 (Replica 1905 design, Museum Collection). 4-½in (12cm); button only without stock label; limited edition 12,000 (ear tag #0085/12). *Photograph courtesy Steiff.* Please refer to page 127 for price guide.

Far left: *Betty Tennis Lady* (Back left). 1986 (Replica 1913 design). 17-½in (45cm); white S.L.; limited edition 3,000 (ear tag #9100/45). *Gentleman in Morning Coat* (Back right). 1986 (Replica 1914 design). 19-½in (50cm); white S.L.; limited edition 3,000 (ear tag #9102/50). *Jackie* (Front left). 1986 (Replica 1953 design). 10in (25cm); white S.L.; limited edition. 10,000 (ear tag #0190/25). *Polar Bear* (Front right). 1987 (Replica 1909 design, Museum Collection). 4-¼in (11cm); button only without stock label; limited edition 3,000 (ear tag #0090/11). *Photograph courtesy Steiff.* Please refer to pages 128–130 for price guide.

Top right: Tabby Cat (Left). 1986 (Replica 1928 design, Museum Collection). 4in (10cm); button in ear without stock label; limited edition 6,000 (ear tag #0104/10). *Teddy Clown* (Center). 1986 (Replica 1926 design). 12-½in (32cm); white S.L.; limited edition 10,000 (ear tag #0170/32). *Bully Dog* (Right). 1986 (Replica 1927 design, Museum Collection). 5-½in (14cm); button only without stock label; limited edition 6,000 (ear tag #0101/14). *Photograph courtesy Steiff.* Please refer to pages 128–129 for price guide.

Above left: *Teddy Rose Bear.* 1987 (Replica 1925 design). 16in (41cm); pink mohair; "center seam" head; brown stitched nose; mouth and claws; plastic eyes; f.j.; e.s.; B.B.; white cloth weave S.L. Limited edition 10,000. CONDITION: Mint. PRICE: $700. *Courtesy Ho Phi Le.*

Above right: *Classic 1907 Teddy Bear.* 1996. 15-¾in (40cm); cinnamon mohair; plastic eyes; f.j.; s.s.; yellow S.L.; (ear tag # 027673); knitted outfit. *St. Bernard Dog.* 1996. 5-¼in (13cm); brown and white mohair; plastic eyes; n.j.; legs; swivel head; s.s.; yellow S.L.; (ear tag #031625). *Photograph courtesy Steiff.* Please refer to page 144 for price guide.

Top left: **Wiwag-Bear Pull Toy** (Bottom left). 1989 (Replica 1924 design, Museum Collection). 9-½in. (24cm); white S.L.; limited edition 4,000 (ear tag #0132/24). **Baby Bear Pull Toy** (Top left). 1989 (Replica 1939 design, Museum Collection). 8in 20cm); white S.L.; limited edition 4,000 (ear tag #0135/20). **Coloro-Clown** (Right) 1989. (Replica 1911 design). 18in (43cm); white S.L.; limited edition 3,000 (ear tag #9130/43). *Photograph courtesy Steiff.* Please refer to pages 130–132 for price guide.

Bottom left: **Baerle** Bear. 35PB. 1991. (Replica 1903 design). 19-¾in (50cm); distressed cinnamon-colored mohair; shoe-button eyes; simulated sealing wax nose; f.j. (twine thread, jointing cardboard discs); e.s.; B.B.; white S.L. Limited edition 6,000 pieces. This replica was the predecessor to the "Metal Rod Bears": of 1904/1905 (ear tag #0150/50). *Photograph courtesy Steiff.* Please refer to page 134 for price guide.

Top right: **Fox** (Top left). 1989. (Replica 1910 design, Museum Collection). 4-½in (12cm); button in ear without stock label; limited edition 4,000 (ear tag #0093/12). **Donkey with Neck Mechanism** (Bottom left). 1989. (Replica 1931 design, Museum Collection). 8in (20cm); white S.L.; limited edition 4,000 (ear tag #0126/20). **Jumbo Elephant** (Top right). (Replica 1932 design, Museum Collection). 9-¼in (24cm); white S.L.; limited edition 4,000 (ear tag #0125/24). **Pig with Neck Mechanism** (Bottom right). 1989. (Replica 1909 design, Museum Collection). 5-½in (14cm); button in ear without label; limited edition 4,000 (ear tag #0091/14). *Photograph courtesy Steiff.* Please refer to pages 131–132 for price guide.

Bottom right: **Petsy** (Left). 1990. (Replica 1927 design). 13-½in (35cm); white S.L.; limited edition 5,000 (ear tag #0181/35). **Record Teddy** (Right). 1990. (Replica 1913 design, Museum Collection). 10in (25cm); white S.L.; limited edition 4,000 (ear tag #0116/25). *Photograph courtesy Steiff.* Please refer to pages 132–133 for price guide.

Left: *Bicolor Bear*. (Replica 1926 design) (Left)
1990. 25in (65cm); limited edition 5,000. (Right)
1991 15-½in (40cm); limited edition 6,000.
Brown-tipped gray mohair; large plastic eyes; f.j.;
e.s.; B.B.; white S.L (ear tag # 0169/65, 0169/40).
Photograph courtesy Steiff. Please refer to pages
133–134 for price guide.

Right: *Panda Bear*. 1992-1998 (Replica 1938
design). 11-½in (29cm), 13-¾in (35cm);
black/white mohair; B.B.; yellow S.L. (ear tag
#408304, #408311). *Photograph courtesy Steiff.*
Please refer to page 136 for price guide.

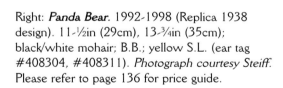

Left: *Music Bear*. 1992. (Replica 1928 design).
15-¾in (40cm); golden yellow mohair; plastic
eyes; f.j.; wood shaving stuffing; white S.L.;
limited edition 8,000 (ear tag #407482). Music
is produced by squeezing musical mechanism
encased in tummy. *Photograph courtesy Steiff.*
Please refer to page 137 for price guide.

Far left: *Louis*. 1994. (Replica 1904 design). 17-½in (44cm); brown mohair; white S.L.; limited edition of 3,500 (ear tag #650789). Comes with Grand Prize Medal. Produced in celebration of the 100th Anniversary of Steiff receiving the Grand Prize Medal at the St. Louis World's Fair. U.S. only. *Photograph courtesy Steiff*. Please refer to page 140 for price guide.

Top right: *Compass Rose*. 1995. 17-½in (44cm); wavy pink mohair; white S.L.; limited edition of 3,500 (ear tag #650819); wearing mariner's compass. Produced in honor of the first America's Cup Women's team. U.S. only. *Photograph courtesy Steiff*. Please refer to page 141 for price guide.

Above left: *Forever Friends*. 1996. 9in (23cm); (left) blue mohair; (right) gray mohair; white S.L.; limited edition of 4,000 (ear tag #665059); U.S. only. *Photograph courtesy Steiff*. Please refer to page 144 for price guide.

Above right: *Jubilee Bear*. 1998. 15-5/8in (40cm); white mohair; glass eyes; f.j.; e.s.; white S.L.; porcelain medallion. Produced in celebration of the 150th birthday of Margaret Steiff. Limited 3,999 (ear tag #670152). CONDITION: Mint. PRICE: $950. *Courtesy Deborah and Donald Ratliff*.

The Walt Disney World conventions, which began in 1988, highlight specific artists' and manufacturers' bears. The Steiff bears produced for Disney conventions are especially valuable because both bear and Disney enthusiasts collect them.

Left: Walt Disney World® 1st Convention Bear. *(Margaret Strong)*. 1988. 12in (32cm); antique gold mohair; white S.L.; B.B.; limited edition 1,000 (ear tag #0243/32). CONDITION: Mint. PRICE: $1,800–up. *Courtesy Yasuhiro Gawase.*

Right: Walt Disney World® 2nd Convention Bear. *(Petsy)*. 1989. 13-¾in (35cm); white mohair; white S.L.; B.B.; limited edition 1,000 (ear tag # 0244/35). CONDITION: Mint. PRICE: $1,000–up. *Courtesy Yasuhiro Gawase.*

Right: Walt Disney World® 3rd Convention Bear. 1990. 12-½in (32cm); charcoal gray mohair; white S.L.; B.B.; limited edition 1,000 (ear tag # 0245/32). CONDITION: Mint. PRICE: $750–up. *Courtesy Yasuhiro Gawase.*

Left: Walt Disney World® 4th Convention Bear. *(Mickey Mouse)*. 1991. 12-½in (32cm); black mohair; *Mickey Mouse* mask; white S.L.; B.B.; limited edition 1,500 (ear tag #0246/32). CONDITION: Mint. PRICE: $1,300–up. *Courtesy Yasuhiro Gawase.*

Right: Walt Disney World® 5th Convention Bear. *(Minnie Mouse)*. 1992. 12-½in (30cm); black mohair; *Minnie Mouse* mask; white S.L.; B.B.; limited edition 1,500 (ear tag #011863). CONDITION: Mint. PRICE: $900–up. *Courtesy Yasuhiro Gawase.*

Far left: Walt Disney World® 6th Convention Bear. (**Donald Duck**). 1993. 11-¾in (30cm); white mohair; designed and dressed to resemble **Donald Duck**; white S.L.; B.B.; limited edition 1,500 (ear tag #651205). CONDITION: Mint. PRICE: $850–up. *Courtesy Yasuhiro Gawase.*

Top right: Walt Disney World® 7th Convention Bear. (**Winnie the Pooh**). 1994. Gold mohair; short sweater; white S.L. Sizes: 11-¾in (30cm); limited edition 2,500 (ear tag #651243). 24in (60cm); limited edition of 25 (ear tag #651250). largest size; limited edition 5 (ear tag #651270). *Courtesy Steiff.* Please refer to page 140 for price guide.

Above left: Walt Disney World® 8th Convention Bear. (**Baloo**). 1995. Beige mohair; white S.L. Sizes: 11in (28cm); limited edition 2,500 (ear tag #651274). 24in (60cm); limited edition 25 (ear tag #651281). *Courtesy Steiff.* Please refer to page 141 for price guide.

Above right: Walt Disney World® 9th Convention Bear. (**Geppetto and Pinocchio**). 1996. **Geppetto** is gold mohair. **Pinocchio** is carved wood; white S.L. (ear tag #651311). Sizes: 13-¾in (25cm); limited edition 1,500. 24in (60cm); limited edition 25. 31-½in (80cm); limited edition 5. *Courtesy Steiff.* Please refer to page 144 for price guide.

Steiff Club

Ninety years after the invention of the first Steiff teddy bear, Steiff took this jubilee as the opportunity to create for him and his friends the forum, which had been planned for years, the Steiff Club.

The Advantages.

- Two exclusive Club editions that are produced every year as limited editions for Club members only. There is no obligation to buy.
- Club members are sent the quarterly *Steiff Club* magazine with a wealth of valuable information about Steiff—tips on auctions, information about special editions, reports by collectors, etc.
- For real Steiff fans, there is a Club collection with interesting accessories such as T-shirts, writing paper and much more.
- Regional Club meetings are held on a regular basis. There, members can discuss their interests, see new products and hear lectures given by specialist speakers.

The Club Team is there to answer your questions:
CONTACT INFORMATION
Steiff Club. Margarete Steiff GmbH
Alleenstrasse 2, D-89537, Giengen, Brenz, Germany
Tel: +49(0)7322/131-427 or 452
Fax: +49(0) 7322/131-476
http://www.steiff.com

For Club inquiries from North America:
Steiff North America, Inc.
425 Paramount Drive
Raynham, MA 02767
Tel: 508-828-2377
Fax: 508-821-4477
Club Line: 800-830-0429

In celebration of the 150th anniversary of the birth of Margarete Steiff, the *Steiff Club Companion's* quarterly newsletter featured this beautiful portrait of Margarete Steiff. *Courtesy Steiff.*

Steiff Club Editions—1992-2000

Far left: First Steiff Club Edition. *Teddy Baby*. Bear. 1992/93 (Replica 1929 design). 11in (28cm); blue mohair; white S.L.; limited edition 7,959 (ear tag #420016); no certificate. *Photograph courtesy Steiff.* Please refer to page 136 for price guide.

Top right: Second Steiff Club Edition. *Teddy Clown*. Bear. 1993/94 (Replica 1928 design). 11in (28cm); brown-tipped white mohair; white S.L.; limited edition 11,020 (ear tag #420023). *Photograph courtesy Steiff.* Please refer to page 139 for price guide.

Above left: First Steiff Club U.S.A. Edition. *Sam*. Bear. 1993. 11in (28cm); gold mohair; white S.L.; limited edition 4.000 (ear tag # 420801). *Photograph courtesy Steiff.* Please refer to page 139 for price guide.

Above right: Third Steiff Club Edition. *Original Steiff Teddy Bear*. 1994/95 (Replica 1908 design). 13-¾in (35cm); blue mohair, white S.L.; limited edition 14,910 (ear tag # 420047). CONDITION: Mint. PRICE: $550. *Photograph courtesy Deborah and Donald Ratliff.*

Steiff Club Editions Not Pictured

Fourth Steiff Club Edition. *Baby Bear*. 1995/96 (Replica 1946 design). 13-¾in (35cm); blonde mohair; limited edition 10,880 (ear tag # 420054). *Camel on Wheels*. 1995/96 (Replica 1930 design). 13-¾in (35cm); limited edition 1,770 (ear tag # 420061). Please refer to page 142 for price guide.

Fifth Steiff Club Edition. *Dicky Brown Bear*. 1996/97 (Replica 1935 design). 12-½in (32cm); brown mohair; limited edition 7,965 (ear tag # 420078). *Poodle with Neck Mechanism*. 1996/97 (Replica 1931 design). 11in (28cm); white mohair; limited edition 3,545 (ear tag # 420085). Please refer to page 145 for price guide.

Sixth Steiff Club Edition. *Picnic Bear*. 1997/98. 13-½in (34cm); gold blond mohair; limited edition 9,888 (ear tag # 420108). *Felt Elephant on Wheels*. 1997/98 (Replica 1914 design). 8-½in (22cm); gray felt; limited edition 3,232 (ear tag # 420115). Please refer to page 148 for price guide.

Seventh Steiff Club Edition. *School Starter Bear*. 1998/99. 11-¾in (30cm); green mohair; limited edition 8,730 (ear tag # 420139). *Horse on Wheels*. 1998/99 (Replica 1929 design). 13-¾in (35cm); brown mohair; limited edition 2,020 (ear tag # 420146). Please refer to page 152 for price guide.

Eighth Steiff Club Edition. *Mourning Bear*. 1999/00 (Replica 1912 design). . Black mohair; limited edition 9,000 (ear tag # 420160). *Polar Bear on Wheels*. 1999/00 (Replica 1910 design). 8-½in (22cm); limited edition 5,600 (ear tag # 420177). Please refer to page 155 for price guide.

Ninth Steiff Club Edition. *Year 2000 Teddy Bear*. 1999/00. (Steiff's first-ever mid-year club exclusive). 12-½in (32cm); golden brown/rose mohair; limited edition 9,450 (ear tag # 420184). Please refer to page 155 for price guide.

Tenth Steiff Club Edition. *Teddy Bear* Harlequin. 1999/00 (Replica 1925 design). 13-¾in (35cm); blue/red mohair; limited edition (ear tag # 420214). Please refer to page 40 for picture of the original one-of-a-kind 1925 Harlequin Bear. *Toy German Spitz*. 1999/00 (Replica 1935 design). 7in (18cm); white mohair; limited edition (ear tag # 420207). Please refer to page 157 for price guide.

Special International Editions—1994-2000

Right: *Masako*. Bear. 1994. 10in (25cm); B.B.; white S.L.; limited edition 1,500 (ear tag #650796). Japan only. CONDITION: Mint. PRICE: $3,000–up. *Courtesy Yasuhiro Gawase.*

Far right: *Taro*. Bear. 1995. 11in (28cm); B.B.; white S.L.; limited edition 2,000. (ear tag #650864). Japan only. CONDITION: Mint. PRICE: $650–up. *Courtesy Yasuhiro Gawase.*

Far left: *Nagano*. Bear. 1997. 11-½in (30cm); B.B.; white S.L.; limited edition 2,500 (ear tag #652592). Japan only. CONDITION: Mint. PRICE: $1,300–up. *Courtesy Yasuhiro Gawase.*

Top right: *U.K. Baby Bear Set.* 1994–1998. 6-¼in (16cm); mohair; f.j.; B.B.; white S.L.; limited edition 1847 (the year of Margarete Steiff's birth). These five bears are miniaturized versions of former U.K. bears. This is a particularly decorative set, with the varying colors of the bears set off by the blue satin lining of the hardwood display box. U.K. only. CONDITION: Mint. PRICE: $635–up. *Courtesy Teddy Bears of Witney.*

Above left: *Baby Alfonzo*. 1995-1997. 9-½in (24cm); red mohair; hand-stuffed wood shavings; B.B.; white S.L.; wearing cotton sateen Cossack tunic, trousers and braces; limited edition 5,000. Made exclusively for Teddy Bears of Witney. *Baby Alfonzo* is a small replica of the original world famous 1908 Steiff red bear *Alfonzo*, purchased in 1989 at Christie's auction by Ian Pout of Teddy Bears of Witney. Grand Duke George Michailovich gave the bear to his daughter, Princess Xenia in 1908. CONDITION: Mint. PRICE: $395–up. *Courtesy Teddy Bears of Witney.*

Above right: *Henderson*. 1997–1999. 22in (55cm); long pile gold mohair; B.B.; white S.L.; limited edition 2,000. Created in honor of Colonel Bob Henderson, co-founder with Jim Ownby of Good Bears of the World. Made exclusively for Teddy Bears of Witney. CONDITION: Mint. PRICE: $499–up. *Courtesy Teddy Bears of Witney.*

Left: Bears. (Left to right) *Lavender Blue Bear*. 1998. 16-½in (42cm); bright lavender wavy mohair; plastic eyes; f.j.; s.s.; white S.L.; limited edition 3,500. U.S.A. only. CONDITION: Mint. PRICE: $350. *Holland's 2nd Tulip Bear*. 1997. 13-1/2in (35cm); bright green mohair; plastic eyes; f.j.; s.s.; limited edition 1,847. CONDITION: Mint. PRICE: $400. *Himbeer Ours Teddy*. 1995. 16in (41cm); raspberry mohair; plastic eyes; f.j.; s.s.; limited edition 1,500. All bears have B.B. with white S.L. CONDITION: Mint. PRICE: $400. *Courtesy Deborah and Donald Ratliff.*

Right: *U.K. Bear 2000*. 16in (40cm); white mohair; gold stitched nose, mouth and claws; f.j.; e.s.; B.B.; white S.L.; limited edition 4,000. U.K. only. CONDITION: Mint. PRICE: $245. *Courtesy Teddy Bears of Witney.*

Left: *George*. 2000. 12in (30cm); gold mohair; f.j.; traditionally hand-stuffed with wood shaving; white S.L.; "gold-plated" button in ear; limited edition 2,000; comes with felt drawstring bag. *George* is exclusively made for Teddy Bears of Witney, and is the first Steiff limited edition bear produced in the new millennium. Named after St. George, the patron Saint of England. CONDITION: Mint. PRICE: $225–up. *Courtesy Teddy Bear of Witney.*

Price Guide

Museum Replicas, Special and Limited Editions—1980-2001

Item Ear tag# EAN #	Sortiment Book Vol#1	Vol#2	Year	Description	Value

1980-1982

Item Ear tag# EAN #	Vol#1	Vol#2	Year	Description	Value
0153/43	393	414	1980	PAPA BEAR 17in (43cm). Limited 11,000 (5,000 with a certificate in English) white tag, boxed, replica 1903, 100th Anniversary, first boxed limited edition, Worldwide.	$950.00
0155/38	385	457	1981	MAMA AND BABY SET 15in (38cm) and 6in (15cm) Limited 8,000, white tag, boxed, certificate, replica 1903, Steiff's 101st anniversary, the baby does not have an ear tag. U.S.A only.	$600.00
0223/30	386	465	1982/84	BRUNO BEAR 11-¾in (30cm). Yellow tag. Replica of a teddy bear from the past, U.S.A. only.	$250.00
0155/26 404597	384	465	1982/90 1991/99	MARGARET STRONG BEAR GOLD 10-¼in (26cm). U.S.A. only. Current Ear Tag $120.00 Old Ear Tag $145.00	
0155/32 404627	384	465	1982/91 1991/99	MARGARET STRONG BEAR GOLD 12-½in (32cm). U.S.A. only. Limited 20,000, white tag, replica 1904, boxed, not issued with a certificate. Current Ear Tag $150.00 Old Ear Tag $275.00	
0204/16	385	457	1982/85	TEA PARTY SET 6-¼in (16cm) each Limited 10,000, boxed, certificate, 102nd Anniversary, four bears, white, dark brown, honey and caramel, Steiff logo tea set, all have the same ear tag number. U.S.A. only.	$550.00
0203/00	385	457	1982	WHITE TEDDY BEAR SERIES 4-¼in (11cm), 6-½in (18cm), 10-¼in (26cm), 12-½in (32cm) and 16in (41cm). Limited 2,000, white tag, boxed, set of 5 bears, felt paws, U.S.A. only.	$500.00

1983

Item Ear tag# EAN #	Vol#1	Vol#2	Year	Description	Value
0118/25	68	489	1983/87	BOXER DOG 10in (25cm). Limited 2,000, yellow tag, U.S.A. only.	$165.00
0165/38 406331	393	424	1983/88	1909 GOLD TEDDY BEAR 15in (38cm) Yellow tag, Worldwide.	$325.00
0165/51	393	424	1983/88	1909 GOLD TEDDY BEAR 20in (51cm). Yellow tag, Worldwide.	$650.00
0140/38	386	465	1983	KLEIN ARCHIE BEAR 15in (38cm) Limited 2,500, made for Enchanted Doll House, Vermont, U.S.A. only.	$295.00
8020/00	408	489	1983/85	MANNI RABBIT SET 4in (10cm), 8in (20cm) and 11-¾in (30cm) Limited 2,000, white tag, boxed, standing in a begging position, U.S.A. only.	$325.00
0310/19	22		1983/85	MANSCHLI OR BUDDHA BEAR 7-¼in (19cm). Yellow tag, U.S.A. only.	$300.00
0155/42 404832	384	465	1983/90 1991/99	MARGARET STRONG BEAR GOLD 16-½in (42cm). U.S.A. only. Yellow tag, replica 1904 bear, U.S.A. only. Current Ear Tag $220.00 Old Ear Tag $395.00	
0160/00	384	457	1983	MARGARET STRONG CHOCOLATE BROWN SET 7in (18cm), 10in (26cm), 12-½in (32cm) and 16-½in (42cm). Limited 2,000, white tag, boxed, U.S.A. only.	$850.00
0210/22	385	457	1983	NIMROD TEDDY ROOSEVELT COMMEMORATIVE SET 9in (22cm) each bear Limited 10,000, white tag, boxed, certificate, three bears, white, gold, caramel, dressed, for the 125th birthday of Teddy Roosevelt and 80th birthday of teddy bear, U.S.A. only.	$450.00
0150/32	393	414	1983/84	RICHARD STEIFF BEAR 12-½in (32cm). Limited Edition 20,000, white tag, boxed, not issued with a certificate, replica 1902-1903 for the 80th birthday of the teddy bear, Worldwide.	$550.00

Item Ear tag# EAN #	Sortiment Book Vol#1	Vol#2	Year	Description	Value
0112/17	408	489	1983/87	TIGER 6-½in (17cm). Yellow tag, limited 2,000, replica 1953, U.S.A. only.	$200.00
0112/28	408	489	1983/87	TIGER 11in (28cm). Yellow tag, limited 2,000, replica 1953, U.S.A. only.	$300.00
0130/17	408	490	1983/84	UNICORN 6-½in (17cm). Limited 2,000, white tag, U.S.A. only.	$350.00
0130/27	408	490	1983/84	UNICORN 10-½in (27cm). Limited 2,000, white tag, U.S.A. only.	$295.00

1984

Item Ear tag# EAN #	Sortiment Book Vol#1	Vol#2	Year	Description	Value
8495/03	464		1984/86	BEAR PIN HEAD Beige, 1-¼in (4cm)	$100.00
8496/03	464		1984/86	BEAR PIN HEAD Caramel, 1-¼in (4cm)	$100.00
8497/03	464		1984/86	BEAR PIN HEAD White, 1-¼in (4cm)	$100.00
8498/03	464		1984/88	BEAR PIN HEAD Chocolate, 1-¼in (4cm)	$100.00
0162/00 405808	393	414	1984/87	GIENGEN TEDDY SET OR BIRTHPLACE OF THE TEDDY 4in (10cm), 12-½in (32cm) Limited 16,000, white tag, boxed, certificate, mama and baby, Worldwide.	$425.00
0165/28	393	424	1984/86	1909 GOLD TEDDY BEAR 11in (28cm). Yellow tag, Worldwide.	$250.00
0165/60	393	424	1984/86	1909 GOLD TEDDY BEAR 23-½in (60cm). Yellow tag, Worldwide.	$850.00
0173/ 25,30,32		458	1984	GOLDILOCKS AND THE THREE BEARS (large set) 16in (41cm), 12-½in (32cm), 11-¾in (30cm) and 10in (25cm). Limited 2,000, white tag, boxed, large set Susan Gibson doll and papa, mama and baby bear, (Made for Reeves International) U.S.A. only.	$850.00
0155/00	408	490	1984/86	HOPPY RABBIT SET 3in (8cm), 5-½in (14cm) and 6-½in (17cm) Limited 2,000, white tag, boxed, running position, U.S.A. only.	$325.00
0111/21 402425	408	428	1984/86	LION 8-¼in (21cm) Limited 2,000, yellow tag, replica 1956, U.S.A. only.	$175.00
0111/35 402449	408	428	1984/86	LION 13-¾in (35cm) Limited 1,000, yellow tag, replica 1956, U.S.A. only. Also 1992 Lion 402463	$225.00
0155/37	383		1984/89	MARGARET STRONG GROOM BEAR 14-½in (37cm). Yellow tag, boxed, U.S.A. only.	$400.00
0155/36	383		1984/89	MARGARET STRONG BRIDE BEAR 14in (36cm). Yellow tag, boxed, U.S.A. only.	$400.00
0156/00	384	458	1984	MARGARET STRONG CINNAMON SET 7in (18cm), 10-¼in (26cm), 12-½in (32cm) and 16-½in (42cm). Limited 2,000, white tag, boxed, certificate, U.S.A. only.	$850.00
0157/26	384	466	1984/86	MARGARET STRONG CREAM BEAR 10-¼in (26cm). Yellow Tag, U.S.A. only.	$200.00
0157/32	384	466	1984/86	MARGARET STRONG CREAM BEAR 12-½in (32cm). Yellow tag, U.S.A. only.	$325.00
0157/42	384	466	1984/86	MARGARET STRONG CREAM BEAR 16-½in (42cm). Yellow tag, U.S.A. only.	$450.00
0155/51 404863	384	465	1984/90 1991/99	MARGARET STRONG GOLD BEAR 20in (51cm). U.S.A. only. Current Ear Tag $350.00 Old Ear Tag $495.00	
0155/60 404894	384		1984/90 1991	MARGARET STRONG GOLD BEAR 23-¾in (60cm). U.S.A. only. Yellow tag, replica 1904 bear, currently available. Current Ear Tag $450.00 Old Ear Tag $550.00	
0080/08 400025	408	414	1984/87	MUSEUM FELT ELEPHANT 3in (8cm) Limited 10,000, button only, boxed, replica 1880. U.S.A. only.	$175.00
0082/20 400247	393	414	1984/87	MUSEUM ROLY-POLY BEAR Replica 1894, 8in (20cm) Limited 9,000, button only, boxed, replica 1898.	$250.00
0151/25	387	466	1984/86	MR. CINNAMON BEAR 10in (25cm). Yellow tag, 1903 replica. U.S.A. only.	$350.00
0151/32	387	466	1984/85	MR. CINNAMON BEAR 12-½in (32cm). Yellow tag, 1903 replica. U.S.A. only.	$450.00
0151/40	387	466	1984/85	MR. CINNAMON BEAR 15-¾in (40cm). Yellow tag, 1903 replica. U.S.A. only.	$600.00
0151/55	387	466	1984	MR. CINNAMON BEAR 21-½in (55cm). Yellow tag, 1903 replica. Germany only.	$1,200.00
0201/10	385	466	1984/85	ORIGINAL TEDDY BEAR Beige, 4in (10cm). Yellow tag.	$100.00
0202/10	385	466	1984/85	ORIGINAL TEDDY BEAR Caramel, 4in (10cm). Yellow tag.	$100.00
0203/10	385	466	1984/85	ORIGINAL TEDDY BEAR White, 4in (10cm). Yellow tag.	$100.00
0206/10	385	466	1984/85	ORIGINAL TEDDY BEAR Chocolate, 4in (10cm). Yellow tag.	$100.00

Item Ear tag# EAN #	Sortiment Book Vol#1	Vol#2	Year	Description	Value
0225/42	387	468	1984/89	OPHELIA BEAR 16-½in (42cm) Issued button only, tag on the leg, not issued with a box, U.S.A. only.	$450.00
0178/29	386	466	1984/85	PANDA BEAR 11-¼in (29cm). Yellow tag, replica 1938, reissued 1992.	$295.00
0178/35	386	466	1984/85	PANDA BEAR 13-¾in (35cm). Yellow tag, replica 1938, reissued 1992.	$400.00
7635/19	382	484	1984/88	SANTA CLAUS DOLL 7-½in (19cm). Also see 1985 Santa # 7635/28.	$175.00
0175/29	386	466	1984/89	TEDDY BABY BROWN 11-¼in (29cm). Yellow tag, replica 1930, U.S.A. only.	$250.00
0175/35	386	466	1984/90	TEDDY BABY BROWN 13-¾in (35cm). Yellow tag, also 1991 407758	$350.00
0175/42	386	466	1984/89	TEDDY BABY BROWN 16-½in (42cm). Yellow tag, replica 1930, U.S.A. only.	$495.00

1985

Item Ear tag# EAN #	Sortiment Book Vol#1	Vol#2	Year	Description	Value
0251/34	386	467	1985/87	BERLIN BEAR 13-½in (34cm). Yellow tag, boxed, U.S.A. only.	$275.00
0172/32 407505	394	414	1985/88	DICKY BEAR 12-½in (32cm) Limited 20,000, white tag, replica 1930, Worldwide.	$350.00
0172/32	390	458	1985/86	DICKY CLOWNS AROUND 12-½in (32cm). Limited 100, yellow tag, very rare, made for Ronald McDonald House, Dicky bear is dressed as Ronald McDonald, U.S.A. only.	$3,000.00
0167/32	387		1985/89	1906 GRAY GIENGEN BEAR 12in (32cm). Yellow tag, replica 1906, light gray. U.S.A. only.	$225.00
0167/42	387	467	1985/89	1906 GRAY GIENGEN BEAR 16in (42cm). Yellow tag, light gray, replica 1906, U.S.A. only. Also see Gray Giengen Bears 1986 #0167/22 and 0167/52.	$350.00
0173/ 22,18,14		458	1985	GOLDILOCKS AND THE THREE BEARS 8-½in (22cm), 7in (18cm) and 5-½in (14cm) Limited 5,000, white tag, small set, Susan Gibson doll, boxed, three Steiff bears, Papa, Mama, Baby.	$550.00
0211/26	386	467	1985	LUV BEAR-ER 10-¼in (26cm)	$175.00
0211/36	386	467	1985	LUV BEAR-ER 14in (36cm) Yellow tag, dressed in a yellow felt vest with embroidered red heart, difficult to find, U.S.A. only.	$195.00
0157/51	384	466	1985/86	MARGARET STRONG CREAM BEAR 20in (51cm). Yellow tag, U.S.A. only.	$800.00
0157/60	384	466	1985/86	MARGARET STRONG CREAM BEAR 23-½in (61cm). Yellow tag, U.S.A. only.	$1,300.00
0155/23	383		1985/87	MARGARET STRONG RING BEAR-ER 9in (23cm). Yellow tag, boxed, U.S.A. only.	$250.00
0155/22	383		1985/87	MARGARET STRONG FLOWER BEAR-ER 8-½in (22cm). Yellow tag, boxed, U.S.A. only.	$250.00
0158/25	384	458	1985/88	MARGARET STRONG WHITE LEATHER PAW BEAR 10in (25cm) Limited 3,000, white tag, U.S.A. only.	$300.00
0158/31	384	458	1985/88	MARGARET STRONG WHITE LEATHER PAW BEAR 12in (31cm) Limited 2,500, white tag, U.S.A. only.	$400.00
0158/41	384	458	1985/88	MARGARET STRONG WHITE LEATHER PAW BEAR 16in (41cm) Limited 2,000, white tag, U.S.A. only. Also see 1986 for largest size made 0158/50	$600.00 $2,000.00
0277/28	N/A		1985	MARSHALL FIELD'S HANS (BOY) 11in (28cm). Limited 5,000, white tag, boxed, dressed in lederhose. Special for Marshall Fields Store, U.S.A. only.	$250.00
0278/28	N/A		1985	MARSHALL FIELD'S HELGA (GIRL) 11in (28cm) Limited 5,000 white tag, boxed, special for Marshall Fields Store. U.S.A. only.	$300.00
0085/12 400377	393	414	1985/87	MUSEUM BEAR ON WHEELS 4-½in (12cm) Limited 12,000, button only, boxed, replica 1905.	$200.00
0105/17 401251	409	428	1985/87	MUSEUM PENGUIN 5-½in (17cm). Limited 8,000, button only, boxed, replica 1928.	$200.00
134/22	408	428	1985	NIKI RABBIT 8-½in (22cm). Yellow tag, replica 1952. Limited 3,500.	$225.00
0134/28	408	428	1985	NIKI RABBIT 11in (28cm). Yellow tag, replica 1952. Limited 2,500 Also see 1992 Niki #402159.	$275.00
0207/10	385		1985/86	ORIGINAL TEDDY BEAR Gray 4in (10cm). Yellow tag.	$100.00
0208/10	385		1985/86	ORIGINAL TEDDY BEAR Black 4in (10cm). Yellow tag.	$100.00

Item Ear tag# EAN #	Sortiment Book Vol#1 Vol#2		Year	Description	Value
0245/40	22	25	1985/88	**PASSPORT BEAR** 15-¼in (41cm) Yellow tag, includes a passport booklet in a vinyl holder around its neck, Worldwide.	$325.00
7635/28	382		1985/88	**SANTA CLAUS DOLL** 11in (28cm). Limited 1,200, white tag, replica 1950.	$195.00
0176/29	386	467	1985/86	**TAN TEDDY BABY** 11-¼in (29cm). Yellow tag. U.S.A. only.	$300.00
0176/35	386	467	1985/86	**TAN TEDDY BABY** 13-¾in (35cm). Yellow tag. U.S.A. only.	$395.00
0176/42	386	467	1985/86	**TAN TEDDY BABY** 16-½in (42cm). Yellow tag. U.S.A. only.	$495.00

1986

Item			Year	Description	Value
4006		490	1986	**ALICE AND HER FRIENDS** Limited 3,000 sets, white tag. Many sets are broken up and the animals are sold separately.	$300.00
0146/13		490	1986	**ALICE CAT** 5in (13cm)	$95.00
0148/13		490	1986	**ALICE MOUSE** 5in (13cm)	$75.00
0147/20		490	1986	**ALICE RABBIT** 8in (20cm)	$100.00
8494/03	387		1986/88	**BEAR PIN HEAD** Gold 1-¼in (4cm)	$100.00
0100/86	378	479	1986/88	**CALLIOPE AND ELEPHANT** Limited 5,000, white tag, boxed and certificate. Elephant only #0135/22.	$1,200.00
0168/22	387	468	1986/88	**1906 GOLD GIENGEN BEAR** 8-½in (22cm). Yellow tag, U.S.A. only.	$250.00
0168/32			1988	**1906 GOLD GIENGEN BEAR** 12in (32cm). Yellow tag, Worldwide.	$350.00
0168/42	387	468	1986/88	**1906 GOLD GIENGEN BEAR** 16-½in (42cm). Yellow tag, U.S.A. only.	$500.00
0167/22	387	467	1986/90	**1906 GRAY GIENGEN BEAR** 8-½in (22cm). Yellow tag, light gray, replica 1906.	$175.00
0167/52	387	467	1986/89	**1906 GRAY GIENGEN BEAR** 20-½in (52cm). Yellow tag, light gray, replica 1906. U.S.A.only. **Also see Gray Giengen Bears 1986 # 0167/32 and #0167/42.**	$450.00
0190/25 408502	394	415	1986/87	**JACKIE BEAR** 10in (25cm) Limited 10,000, white tag, boxed, certificate, Worldwide.	$250.00
0155/15	383	486	1986/87	**MARGARET STRONG CHRISTENING BEAR** 6in (15cm). Yellow tag, boxed, U.S.A. only.	$250.00
0155/38	382	484	1986/89	**MARGARET STRONG SANTA BEAR** 15in (38cm) Yellow tag, boxed, dressed in traditional U.S. Santa's outfit. Replica 1904. **Also see 1987 St. Nickolas # 0156/38 U.S.A. only.**	$400.00
0155/34	383	486	1986	**MARGARET STRONG VICTORIAN GIRL BEAR** 13-½in (34cm)	$400.00
0155/35	383	486	1986	**MARGARET STRONG VICTORIAN BOY BEAR** 13-¾in (35cm) Yellow tag, boxed, certificate, replica 1904, U.S.A. only. **Also see 1987 Victorian Lady # 0156/36 and Victorian Man #0156/37.**	$400.00
0158/50	384	458	1986	**MARGARET STRONG WHITE LEATHER PAW BEAR** 19-½in (50cm). Limited 750, white tag, U.S.A. only.	$2,000.00
0101/14 400957	409	428	1986/87	**MUSEUM BULLY DOG** 5-½in (14cm) Limited 6,000, button only, boxed, replica 1927.	$250.00
0104/10 401237	409	428	1986/88	**MUSEUM TABBY CAT** 4in (10cm) Limited 6,000, button only, boxed, replica 1928.	$250.00
0165/38	N/A		1986	**RINGMASTER BEAR** 15in (38cm). Limited 255, yellow tag, 1909 gold bear. Special for a store in Southern California signing session for Hans Otto Steiff. The outfit was made by Vera Oliver Fuchs. Red jacket, white bib, black top hat, special printed tag on arm, reading "Steiff Ringmaster Admit One" with "Limited Edition #listed."	$600.00
0210/10	385		1986	**ORIGINAL TEDDY BEAR** Light Gold, 4in (10cm). Yellow tag. Germany only.	$100.00
0213/10	385		1986	**ORIGINAL TEDDY BEAR** Cinnamon, 4in (10cm). Yellow tag.	$100.00
0214/10	385		1986	**ORIGINAL TEDDY BEAR** Gold, 4in (10cm). Yellow tag. Both the charcoal and cinnamon were issued with the same numbers.	$100.00

Item Ear tag# EAN #	Sortiment Book Vol#1	Vol#2	Year	Description	Value
0270/28	363	361	1986/88	**TEDDY BRIDE BEAR** 11in (28cm)	$250.00
0271/28	363	361	1986/88	**TEDDY GROOM BEAR** 11in (28cm) Open edition, yellow tag, boxed, dressed Petsy bear.	$250.00
0170/32 407253	393	414	1986/87	**TEDDY CLOWN BEAR** 12-½in (32cm) Limited 10,000, white tag, replica 1926, boxed, certificate, U.S.A. only.	$450.00
0275/28	363	361	1986	**TEDDY "DIRNDL" GIRL BEAR** 11in (28cm). Yellow tag, boxed, Worldwide.	$250.00
0276/28 010170	363	361	1986/89	**TEDDY "LEDERHOSE" BOY BEAR** 11in (28cm) Yellow tag, boxed, dressed Petsy bear. Worldwide.	$250.00
0280/28 010200	363	361	1986/89	**TEDDY SAILOR BOY BEAR** 11in (28cm) Open edition, yellow tag, boxed.	$250.00
0281/28 010224	363	361	1986/89	**TEDDY SAILOR GIRL BEAR** 11in (28cm) Open edition, yellow tag, boxed.	$250.00

1987

Item Ear tag# EAN #	Sortiment Book Vol#1	Vol#2	Year	Description	Value
0255/35	387	468	1987/89	**CLIFFORD BERRYMAN BEAR** 13-¾in (35cm) Yellow tag, Linda Mullins' special piece, difficult to find, U.S.A. only.	$400.00
0164/32	378		1987/89	**CIRCUS DOLLY GREEN BEAR** 12-½in (32cm)	$350.00
0164/34	378	480	1987/89	**CIRCUS DOLLY VIOLET BEAR** 13-¼in (34cm) Limited 2,000, white tag, replica 1913, U.S.A. only.	$350.00
0164/30	378	480	1987	**CIRCUS DOLLY MISTAKE PALE YELLOW BEAR** 11-¾in (30cm) Limited 480, white tag, replica 1913, U.S.A. only.	$650.00
0164/31	378	480	1987/89	**CIRCUS DOLLY YELLOW BEAR** 12in (31cm). White tag.	$350.00
0162/33	389	471	1987	**F.A.O. SCHWARZ 1ST 1906 CHOCOLATE BEAR** 13in (33cm) Limited 1,000, white tag, 125th Anniversary, boxed, certificate.	$395.00
9102/50 412400	412	509	1987/90	**GENTLEMAN IN MORNING COAT** 19-½in (50cm). Limited 3,000	$350.00
9112/45 412509	412	509	1987/90	**PEASANT MAN** 17-½in (45cm)	$375.00
9110/43 412202	412	509	1987/9	**PEASANT LADY** 17in (43cm)	$375.00
9100/45 412301	412	509	1987/90	**BETTY TENNIS LADY** 17-½in (45cm). Limited 2,000, white tag, boxed, certificate, replica 1913, special two buttons one brass and one silver raised script, Worldwide.	$350.00
0201/14	389	469	1987	**HANS HELPER BEAR** 5-½in (14cm) Limited 200, yellow tag, dressed for Steiff Festival Hobby Center Toy Store, Toledo, Ohio.	$350.00
0100/87	378	479	1987/88	**LION WAGON** Limited 5,000, white tag, boxed, certificate. Lion only. 6in (15cm), #0136/15	$350.00
7101	N/A		1987	**LITTLE RED RIDING HOOD AND WOLF SET**	$195.00
0156/38	382		1987/89	**MARGARET STRONG ST. NICHOLAS BEAR** 15in (38cm) Yellow tag, boxed, dressed in traditional Victorian Santa's outfit, replica 1904, U.S.A. only.	$450.00
0156/36	383	486	1987/89	**MARGARET STRONG VICTORIAN LADY BEAR** 14in (36cm)	$400.00
0156/37	383	486	1987/89	**MARGARET STRONG VICTORIAN MAN BEAR** 14-½in (37cm). Yellow tag, boxed, replica 1904, U.S.A. only. **Also see 1986 Victorian Girl # 0155/34 and Victorian Boy # 0155/35**	$400.00
4006	N/A		1987	**MARY AND HER LAMB SET**	$175.00
N/A		469	1987	**MR. SANTA OR NICKLAUS BEAR** Limited 300, yellow tag, this dressed Mr. Santa was also offered at the first year of the Steiff Festival in Toledo, Ohio, for Hobby Center Toys, U.S.A. only.	$450.00
N/A		469	1987	**MRS. SANTA BEAR** Limited 150, yellow tag, first year, special dressed piece for the Steiff Festival in Toledo, Ohio, for Hobby Center Toy Store, by Beth and Ben Savino, U.S.A. only.	$450.00

Item Ear tag# EAN #	Sortiment Book Vol#1 Vol#2		Year	Description	Value
0090/11 **400568**	394	**415**	1987/88	<u>MUSEUM POLAR BEAR</u> 4-¼in (11cm) Limited 3,000, button only, boxed, replica 1909.	$375.00
4007	N/A		1987	<u>ROSE RED AND SNOW WHITE DOLL AND BEAR SET</u> Bear only, white tag.	$300.00 $250.00
0284/28 **010279**	363		1987	<u>TEDDY FARMER BOY BEAR</u> 11in (28cm) Yellow tag, boxed, dressed Petsy bear, U.S.A. only.	$250.00
0163/19	380	**480**	1987	<u>TEDDY CLOWN JR. OR CLOWN TEDDY</u> 7in (19cm) Limited 5,000 total, 2,000 white tag and 3,000 yellow tag, gold mohair, checked outfit.	$250.00
0283/28 **010255**	363		1987	<u>TEDDY BLACK FOREST GIRL BEAR</u> 11in (28cm) Yellow tag, boxed, dressed Petsy bear, U.S.A. only.	$250.00
0171/41 **407208**	394	**415**	1987/89	<u>TEDDY ROSE</u> 16in (41cm) Limited 10,000, boxed, certificate, replica 1925, 1987 U.S.A. only, 1988 Worldwide.	$700.00
0227/33	387	**468**	1987/89	<u>SCHNUFFY BEAR REPLICA 1907</u> 13in (33cm). Issued button only, U.S.A. only.	$450.00
0166/29	399	**453**	1987	<u>WILLIAM SHAKESPEARE BEAR</u> 11-½in (29cm) Limited 2,000, white tag, 1909 style, blond mohair, U. K. only.	$275.00

1988

Item Ear tag# EAN #	Sortiment Book Vol#1 Vol#2		Year	Description	Value
0225/27	387	**468**	1988/90	<u>BABY OPHELIA BEAR</u> 10-½in (27cm). Issued button only, U.S.A. only.	$325.00
0173/40 **406003**	395	**415**	1988/89	<u>BLACK BEAR REPLICA 1907</u> 15-¾in (40cm) Limited 4,000, white tag, boxed, certificate, (short smooth mohair fur, leather nose). U.S.A. only.	$650.00
0166/25	394	424	1988/90	<u>1909 BLOND TEDDY</u> 10in (25cm). Yellow tag, Worldwide.	$115.00
406201		424	1991/92	<u>1909 BLOND TEDDY</u> 10in (25cm). Yellow tag, Worldwide.	$115.00
000355		424	1993/99	<u>1909 BLOND TEDDY</u> 10in (25cm). Yellow tag, Worldwide.	$115.00
0166/35	394	424	1988/90	<u>1909 BLOND TEDDY</u> 13-¾in (35cm). Yellow tag, Worldwide.	$155.00
406225		424	1991/92	<u>1909 BLOND TEDDY</u> 13-¾in (35cm). Yellow tag, Worldwide.	$155.00
000379		424	1993/99	<u>1909 BLOND TEDDY</u> 13-¾in (35cm). Yellow tag, Worldwide.	$155.00
0166/43	394	424	1988/90	<u>1909 BLOND TEDDY</u> 17in (43cm). Yellow tag, Worldwide.	$240.00
406256		424	1991/92	<u>1909 BLOND TEDDY</u> 17in (43cm). Yellow tag, Worldwide.	$240.00
000393		424	1993/99	<u>1909 BLOND TEDDY</u> 17in (43cm). Yellow tag, Worldwide.	$240.00
0156/34	388	**468**	1988/89	<u>CAPTAIN STRONG BEAR</u> 13-¼in (34cm) Yellow tag, boxed, dressed, Margaret Strong replica 1904, U.S.A. only.	$350.00
0120/19	379	481	1988/89	<u>CIRCUS BEAR BANDMASTER</u> 7in (19cm)	$225.00
0122/19	379	481	1988/89	<u>CIRCUS CAT BANDSMAN</u> 7in (19cm)	$200.00
0124/19	379	481	1988/89	<u>CIRCUS CROCODILE BANDSMAN</u> 7in (19cm)	$200.00
0121/19	379	481	1988/89	<u>CIRCUS DOG BANDSMAN</u> 7in (19cm)	$200.00
0123/19	379	481	1988/89	<u>CIRCUS LION BANDSMAN</u> 7in (19cm) Limited 5,000, boxed, white tag, U.S.A. only.	$200.00
9130/43 **412189**	412	**509**	1988/90	<u>COLORO-CLOWN DOLL</u> 18in (43cm) Limited 3,000, white tag, replica 1911, boxed, certificate.	$495.00
0243/32	389	**475**	1988	<u>DISNEY WORLD 1ST CONVENTION BEAR ANTIQUE GOLD</u> 12in (32cm). Limited 1,000, white tag, Margaret Strong Bear, suede paws, for Disney World Epcot Center. U.S.A. only. **Also made a special 7 foot (213cm) size called Hans Willie.**	$1,800.00 $25,000.00
0163/34 **650388**	389	**471**	1988/89	<u>F.A.O. SCHWARZ 1909 WHITE TEDDY BEAR</u> 13in (34cm) Limited 2,000, white tag, boxed, exclusively for F.A.O. Schwarz Toy Store.	$450.00

Item Ear tag# EAN #	Sortiment Book Vol#1 Vol#2	Year	Description	Value
665202	N/A	1997	TEDDY BAR 22 STEIFF FESTIVAL BEAR Limited 100, white tag, special pink mohair bear with a white lace collar and elephant pin, also a birthday cake for Margaret Steiff's 150th birthday celebration, U.S.A. only.	$295.00
404306	420	1997	TEDDY BEAR 1905 19-½in (50cm). Limited 6,000, white tag, red-brown mohair.	$700.00
408434	420	1997	TEDDY BEAR 1951 BLOND 19-½in (50cm). Limited 4,000, white tag, blond mohair.	$600.00
404306		1997/98	TEDDY GIRL 1905 19-½in (50cm) Limited 6,000, white tag, Teddy Girl is a replica of the Teddy Girl that sold for $177,000.00 at the London auction. 1998 Teddy Boy #404320 is a partner to the girl bear.	$1225.00
408328	420	1997	TEDDY VISCOSE BEAR 1948 10in (25cm). Limited 5,000, white tag, blond viscose woven fur.	$275.00
412080	N/A	1997	TRAINER AND ELEPHANT 1911 17in (43cm) Limited 1,200, white tag, felt doll and mohair elephant.	$950.00
651007	439	1997	WIZARD BEAR OR ZAUBARER BEAR 13in (32cm) Limited 2,000, white tag, gray mohair, cape, hat and wand, Germany only.	$300.00

1998

Item Ear tag# EAN #	Sortiment Book Vol#1 Vol#2	Year	Description	Value
651069	441	1998	ACCORDIAN TEDDY BEAR 11-¾in (30cm). Limited 1,500, white tag, gold mohair, dressed in a blue jacket and hat, holding a red accordion, made for Splelzeugring store.	$550.00
658037	457	1998	BELGIUM'S BEACH BEAR 11in (28cm). Limited 1,500, white tag, blue mohair, blue felt paw pads and one is embroidered with 3 interlaced initials BBB, Belgium only.	$275.00
659928	447	1998	BERNER BEAR 13in (32cm) Limited 1,847, white tag, cinnamon, jacket, embroidered paw pads, Switzerland only.	$425.00
659973	449	1998	BRITISH COLLECTOR'S RED BEAR 15-¾in (40cm) Limited 3,000, white tag, red mohair, boxed and certificate, U.K. only.	$395.00
657955	455	1998	BOMMEL BEAR HOLLAND 15-¾in (40cm). Limited 3,000, white tag, Holland only.	$300.00
005015 005022	N/A N/A	1998 1998	CLASSIC APRICOT TEDDY 11in (28cm) Yellow tag. CLASSIC APRICOT TEDDY 15-¾in (40cm) Yellow tag.	$200.00 $275.00
000492 000508	N/A N/A	1998/99 1998/99	CLASSIC 1909 BRASS BEAR 10in (25cm) Yellow tag. CLASSIC 1909 BRASS BEAR 13-¾in (35cm) Yellow tag.	$130.00 $170.00
005077 005121	N/A N/A	1998 1998	CLASSIC CINNAMON TEDDY 11in (28cm) Yellow tag. CLASSIC CINNAMON TEDDY 15-¾in (40cm) Yellow tag.	$200.00 $275.00
005305 005312	N/A N/A	1998 1998	CLASSIC GREEN TEDDY 11in (28cm) Yellow tag. CLASSIC GREEN TEDDY 15-¾in (40cm) Yellow tag.	$200.00 $275.00
005206 005213	N/A N/A	1998 1998	CLASSIC GOLD BLOND TEDDY 11in (28cm) Yellow tag. CLASSIC GOLD BLOND TEDDY 15-¾in (40cm) Yellow tag.	$200.00 $275.00
005060	N/A	1998	CLASSIC LIGHT BLUE TEDDY 11in (28cm) Yellow tag.	$200.00
000300 000317	427 427	1998/99 1998/99	CLASSIC 1907 MOSS GREEN BEAR 10in (25cm) Yellow tag. CLASSIC 1907 MOSS GREEN BEAR 13-¾in (35cm) Yellow tag.	$200.00 $225.00
000171 000188	427 427	1998/99 1998/99	CLASSIC 1903 MR. CINNAMON 8-½in (22cm) Yellow tag. CLASSIC 1903 MR. CINNAMON 11-¾in (30cm) Yellow tag.	$150.00 $200.00
005152 005169	N/A N/A	1998 1998	CLASSIC RED TEDDY 11in (28cm) Yellow tag. CLASSIC RED TEDDY 15-¾in (40cm) Yellow tag.	$200.00 $275.00

Item Ear tag# EAN #	Sortiment Book Vol#1	Vol#2	Year	Description	Value
000263		427	1998	CLASSIC 1907 ROSE BEAR 10in (25cm) Yellow tag.	$200.00
000270		427	1998	CLASSIC 1907 ROSE BEAR 13-3/4in (35cm) Yellow tag.	$225.00
005206	N/A		1998	CLASSIC SILVER GRAY TEDDY 11in (28cm) Yellow tag.	$200.00
005213	N/A		1998	CLASSIC SILVER GRAY TEDDY 15-3/4in (40cm) Yellow tag.	$275.00
037023		508	1998/99	CLASSIC MOLE 10in (25cm). Limited 4,000, white tag, from *"Wind in the Willows,"* black mohair, jointed, dressed in a jacket, pants, white shirt and scarf.	$325.00
037016		508	1998/99	CLASSIC TOAD 10in (25cm). Limited 4,000, white tag, from *"Wind in the Willows,"* green mohair, jointed, dressed in a jacket, pants, white shirt, red vest, and tie.	$325.00
029608		501	1998/99	COMPASS ROSE 6-1/4in (16cm). Yellow tag.	$135.00
652165		473	1998/99	CURIOUS GEORGE 13in (33cm). Limited 2,000, white tag, F.A.O. Schwarz exclusive.	$325.00
665646		474	1998	COLLECTORS UNITED "HAWAIIAN GIRL BEAR" 10-1/4in (26cm). Limited 550, white tag.	$350.00
665653		474	1998	COLLECTORS UNITED "HAWAIIAN GIRL BEAR" 16-1/2in (42cm). Limited 165, white tag.	$650.00
651427		478	1998	DISNEY'S SNOWMAN ORNAMENT Limited 500, white tag, red hat, first Christmas Disney Collectible Convention. **DISNEY WORLD 11TH CONVENTION SEABAR**	$225.00
651380		477	1998	12-1/2in (32cm). Limited 2,000.	$350.00
651397		477	1998	23-1/2in (60cm). Limited 25.	
403		477	1998	31-1/2in (80cm). Limited 5. White tag, lavendar mohair, ceramic medallion made for Disney World Epcot Center, U.S.A. only.	
028564	N/A		1998	DOCTOR BEAR 13-3/4in (35cm). Yellow tag.	$270.00
998713		447	1998	DOLLHOUSE LOGO BEAR BASEL MUSEUM 10in (25cm) Limited 1,500, white tag, blond mohair, Switzerland's Basel museum.	N.P.A.
996733	N/A		1998	DUTCHER FUSSBALL-SUND Limited Edition, white tag, gold curly fur, black pants, Dutcher Fussball-sund printed on a white shirt.	$250.00
670329		443	1998	EURO. CHRISTMAS TREE ORNAMENT BEAR (WHITE 12) 4-1/2in (12cm) Limited 5,000, white tag, white mohair bear, Christmas tree is the same as the American with a cream bear version, European market.	$195.00
652165		473	1998/99	F.A.O. SCHWARZ CURIOUS GEORGE Limited 2,000, white tag. U.S.A. only.	$325.00
200493		473	1998/99	F.A.O. SCHWARZ KING KONG AND MADAME ALEXANDER DOLL Limited 500, white tag. U.S.A. only	$850.00
652219		473	1998	F.A.O. SCHWARZ POLAR BEAR ORNAMENT 5in (12cm). Limited 2,000, white tag.	$225.00
652141		473	1998	F.A.O. SCHWARZ RUDOLPH 9-1/2in (24cm). Limited 2,000, white tag, made from the classic 1939 Robert L. May style, F.A.O. Schwarz exclusive certificate.	$275.00
659959		455	1998	GOUDA BEAR (HOLLAND'S 4TH) 11-3/4in (30cm) Limited 1847, white tag, yellow mohair, holding a cheese tin, boxed and certificate.	$300.00
66009		456	1998	GRAND CRU BEAR VINTAGE (FRANCE) 13in (34cm). Limited 1,500 white tag, boxed, certificate, bordeaux color, gold thread nose, wine tasting plate on red, white and blue ribbon.	N.P.A
652844		451	1998	HAMLEY'S DOMINIC BEAR 11in (28cm). Limited 1,500 white tag, black bear, U.K. only.	$250.00
653186		453	1998	HARRODS GAVOTTE D. POET BEAR 13in (34cm) Limited 2,000, white tag, caramel mohair, white ruffled collar and holding a feather quill.	N.P.A.
653780	N/A		1998	HENDERSON 21-1/2in (55cm). Limited 2,000, white tag, curled gold mohair, center seam, replica Lieutenant-Colonel Robert Henders from the Royal Scots Regiments bear, boxed and certificate, £10 will be donated to the Good Bears Of The World Charity. Teddy Bears of Witney, U.K. only.	$525.00

Item Ear tag# EAN #	Sortiment Book Vol#1	Vol#2	Year	Description	Value
652776		495	1998	LITTLE SANTA BEAR (JAPAN) 8-½in (23cm) Limited 2,500, white tag, wearing a hooded cape, Japan only.	N.P.A.
651076	N/A	442	1998	IDEE SPIEL SCHABARNACK 10-¼in (26cm) Limited 1,500, white tag, gold bear, yellow and blue jester outfit, Idee Spiel, Germany only.	$255.00
670152 670220		441 441 441	1997 1997 1997	JUBILEE BEAR 15-5/8in (40cm). Limited 3,999. JUBILEE BEAR 11-5/8in (30cm). Limited 300. JUBILEE BEAR 21-½in (55cm). Limited 15. Auctioned for Charity only. White tag, porcelin medallion, to celebrate 150th birthday of Margaret Steiff.	$950.00 $1,200.00 N.P.A.
658044		456	1998	LAFAYETE GALLERIES EIFFEL TOWER BEAR 13in (34cm) Limited 1,500, white tag, blue mohair with gold ribbon and holding a metal Eiffel tower.	$525.00
665479	N/A	463	1998	LAVENDER BLUE BEAR 16-½in (42cm). Limited 3,500, white tag, U.S.A. only.	$350.00
028571	N/A		1998	LAWYER BEAR 13-¾in (35cm). Yellow tag.	$270.00
665165	N/A		1998	LITTLE BEAR JACKIE 7in (19cm) Limited 2,500, white tag, small Jackie bear, "The Loving Doll" set, with T-shirt and bear.	$250.00
670084	N/A	441	1998	MARGARET STEIFF MUSEUM BEAR 11-¾in (30cm) Limited 3,050, white tag, porcelain medallion, made for the 1998 visitors of the Steiff Museum.	$180.00
652769		495	1998	MICKEY AND MINNIE DELUXE SET (JAPAN) 11in (28cm) Limited 3,000, white tag, pie eyed set of Mickey, traditional red pants and Minnie in a blue skirt with white polka dots and red and yellow hat, Japan only.	$850.00
651410		478	1998	MICKEY MOUSE CHRISTMAS ORNAMENT 5-½in (14cm) Limited 1,928, white tag, Mickey's 70th birthday, for Disney's catalog, fully jointed, mohair.	$250.00
652721		495	1998	MIFUYU (JAPAN) 11in (28cm). Limited 3000, white tag, special ribbon printed one side"Japan Teddy 1998 Mifuyu," and the other Margaret Steiff GmbH, left paw is embroidered, Japan only.	$295.00
655425	N/A	442	1998	MORGAN POST OR MORNING POST BEAR 12-½in (32cm) Limited 1,500, white tag, blond mohair, gray jacket with green trim and hat, darker gray pants.	$425.00
670114	N/A		1998	M.S. STEIFF BEAR Limited 2,000, white tag, gold mohair, navy blue sweater, blue wool pants and hat, smoking pipe.	$395.00
652592		494	1998	NAGANO JAPAN BEAR 11-¾in (30cm) Limited 2,500, white tag, light gray with white jacket, made for 1998 Winter Olympics.	$850.00
401312	N/A		1998	ORANG-UTAN MIMOCCULO 10in (25cm) Limited 3,000, white tag, rust brown mohair, turntable eyes, Worldwide.	$625.00
996757	N/A		1998	PAMPER'S 25TH ANNIVERSARY BEAR (plush) 11in (28cm)	$99.00
406614		421	1998	PANTOM (PUPPET) BEAR 21-½in (55cm) Limited 4,000, white tag, brown mohair, on a wooden puppet mechanism, Worldwide.	$950.00
000379	N/A	489	1998	RALPH LAUREN HIGHLANDER BEAR Limited 500, yellow tag. As of December 1999 this is the last bear in the series.	$1,000.00
651380	N/A		1998	SEA BAR Limited 2,000, white tag.	$350.00
652714		495	1998	SNOOPY (JAPAN) 10-¼in (26cm).. Limited1,500, white tag, white and black mohair, Japan only.	$695.00
665592		485	1998	SNOWMAN CHRISTMAS ORNAMENT 5in (13cm). Limited 5,000, white tag, U.S.A. only.	$100.00
652783		495	1998	SOCCER BEAR (JAPAN) 13-¾in (35cm). Limited 2,000, white tag, gray mohair T-shirt and pants, paw pad has France 98, made for Soccer Worlds Championship held in France, Japan only.	N.P.A.

Item Ear tag# EAN #	Sortiment Book Vol#1 Vol#2	Year	Description	Value
657962	N/A	1998	**STEIFF BEAR AND HUMMEL FIGURINE** Limited year's production, Christmas Hummel figurine and gold mohair bear with ceramic medallion.	$475.00
420146	514	1998/99	**STEIFF CLUB HORSE ON WHEELS 1929** 13-¾in (35cm) Limited 2,020, Steiff Club members. Yearly fee of $40.00.	$475.00
420139	513	1998/99	**STEIFF CLUB SCHOOL STARTER BEAR** 11-¾in (30cm) Limited 8,730, Steiff Club members. Yearly fee of $40.00, green bear.	$400.00
665196	512	1998/99	**STEIFF CLUB TEDDI SAMMI** 9in (22cm)	$350.00
658051	N/A	1998	**STEIFF CLUB STORE SERNEELS** 17in (43cm) Limited 50, white tag, long curly golden mohair, one paw has the logo of the Belgium Chamber of Commerce, each bear is dressed by Hermes, Louis Vuttion, Delvaux, Ferrari, Bally, Godiva etc. Proceeds will be donated to the Children's Hospital Reine Fabiola.	Auction Price
665370	463	1998	**STRONG TWINS** 6-½in (18cm) Limited 5,000, white tag, light gold mohair, foot pads only, U.S.A. only.	$275.00
665448	478	1998	**SYLVESTER AND TWEETY WARNER BROS #2** 12-½in (32cm) and 5-½in (14cm) Limited 2,500, white tag, made for Warner Bros. Stores.	N.P.A.
039010	501	1998/99	**SX 1909 BRASS TEDDY** 2-¼in (6cm). Yellow tag.	$115.00
039027	501	1998/99	**SX 1909 DARK BROWN TEDDY** 2-¼in (6cm). Yellow tag.	$115.00
039034	501	1998/99	**SX 1909 WHITE TEDDY** 2-¼in (6cm). Yellow tag.	$115.00
039119	501	1998/99	**SX 1909 LIGHT BLOND TEDDY** 2-¼in (6cm). Yellow tag.	$115.00
039126	501	1998/99	**SX 1921 OFF-WHITE TEDDY** 2-¼in (6cm). Yellow tag.	$115.00
039133	501	1998/99	**SX 1921 DARK BROWN TEDDY** 2-¼in (6cm). Yellow tag.	$115.00
039218	502	1998/99	**SX 1930 BLOND TEDDY** 2-1/4in (6cm). Yellow tag.	$115.00
039225	502	1998/99	**SX 1930 TEDDY BABY MAIZE** 2-¼in (6cm). Yellow tag.	$120.00
039232	502	1998/99	**SX 1921 TEDDY BABY BROWN** 2-¼in (6cm). Yellow tag.	$120.00
039317	502	1998/99	**SX 1951 BLOND TEDDY** 2-¼in (6cm). Yellow tag.	$115.00
039324	502	1998/99	**SX 1951 CARAMEL TEDDY** 2-¼in (6cm). Yellow tag.	$115.00
039331	502	1998/99	**SX 1951 DARK BROWN TEDDY** 2-¼in (6cm). Yellow tag.	$115.00
039515	N/A	1998	**12 BEARS WITH DISPLAY RACK**	$1,495.00
039522	N/A	1998	**DISPLAY RACK ONLY**	N.P.A.
652646	496	1998	**TAWIAN STEIFF SPECIAL** 11in (28cm). Limited 1,500, white tag, green-tipped mohair, green ribbon, left paw is embroidered Teddy. Chinese gift box and collectible tea pot with a Chinese Classic written by a famous tea expert from the Tang Dynasty (A.D. 618-907), Taiwan only.	$395.00
652738	495	1998	**TAKARA 10TH ANNIVERSARY BEAR** 8in (21cm). Limited 1,500, white tag.	$425.00
670268	443	1998	**TEDDYBAR NIKOLAUS** 12-½in (32cm). Limited 3,000, white tag, hooded Santa coat.	$375.00
670299	421	1998	**TITANIC POLAR BEAR** Limited 5,000, white tag, white mohair wearing a blue ribbon with a ceramic disk.	$400.00
665615	463	1998	**T. ROOSEVELT AND CUB** 13in (33cm) and 7in (18cm). Limited 4,000, white tag, light gold fur, Safari outfit with a gun, with small Berryman bear, U.S.A. only.	$500.00
655258	N/A	1998	**T.R. GOES WEST** 10-1/2in (27cm). Limited 300, white tag, certificate.	$325.00
670275	421	1998	**TEDDY B (BROWN)** 12-½in (32cm) Limited to year of issue, white tag, brown mohair, white sweater with Teddy B on the front.	$300.00
670282	421	1998	**TEDDY G (GRAY)** 12-½in (32cm) Limited to year of issue, white tag, white mohair, blue sweater with Teddy G on the front.	$300.00
029578	500	1998	**TEDDY 1905 BEAR** 6-¼in (16cm). Yellow tag, red-brown.	$125.00
406508	421	1998	**TEDDY 1909 BEAR** 13-¾in (35cm). Limited 7,000, white tag, dark blue mohair, jointed, Worldwide.	$400.00
029585	500	1998/99	**TEDDY 1920 BEAR** 6-¼in (16cm). Yellow tag, blond.	$125.00
029592	500	1998/99	**TEDDY BEAR BEIGE** 6-¼in (16cm). Yellow tag, beige. US SPECIAL YEAR 1983.	$120.00

Item Ear tag# EAN #	Sortiment Book Vol#1 Vol#2	Year	Description	Value
404320	420	1998	TEDDY BOY 1905 19-½in (50cm). Limited 6,000, white tag, light blond mohair, jointed, Worldwide.	$625.00
404320		1998	TEDDY GIRL 19-½in (50cm) Limited 6,000, white tag, Teddy Girl is a replica of the Teddy Girl that sold for $177,000.00 at the London auction. Also see 1997 Teddy Girl #404306 partner to the boy bear.	$1225.00
665509	463	1998	THE LAST MOHICAN BEAR 8in (20cm) Limited 3,000, white tag, light gold mohair, leather pants, bow and arrows sitting in a wooden canoe.	$275.00
665462	475	1998	QVC TEDDY'S BEAR 11-¾in (30cm) Limited 7,500, white tag, made for the 140th birthday of Theodore Roosevelt.	N.P.A.
659966	446	1998	VIENNA CHORUS BOYS TEDDY BEARS 10-¼in (26cm) Limited 1,847, white tag, 3 bears dressed like the Vienna Chorus Boys, to celibate the 500th Anniversary.	N.P.A.
655340	444	1998	WHITEY GEINGEN FESTIVAL BEAR 11in (28cm) Limited 3,000, white tag, Teddy Baby, white mohair, Germany only.	$550.00
998645	N/A	1998	YAYA BIRD 6-½in (17cm standing) Limited 1,500, white tag, German mountain bike project, blue fur body and jointed yellow fur head, blue felt wings, red felt feathers and legs, gray felt beak, Germany and Switzerland only.	$195.00
652790	494	1998	YUKATA (JAPAN) Limited 1,500, white tag, dressed in a traditional blue and white Kimono with a red sash, made for the Japan Teddy Bear Association, Japan only.	$350.00

1999

Item Ear tag# EAN #	Sortiment Book Vol#1 Vol#2	Year	Description	Value
665882	485	1999	ALL WRAPPED UP CHRISTMAS ORNAMENT 4in (10cm) Limited 5,000, white tag, #6 in series, U.S.A. only.	$110.00
651908	471	1999	ANNO TOY STORE'S FESTIVAL BEAR 13-½in (34cm). Limited 1,500, white tag, honey mohair, green eyes, special bronze medallion, black velvet presentation bag and certificate.	$250.00
665547	469	1999	BIRTHDAY BEAR 13-¾in (35cm). Open edition, U.S.A. only.	$300.00
660047	449	1999	BRITISH COLLECTOR'S LILAC TEDDY BEAR 14in (36cm) Limited 3,000, white tag, lilac long mohair.	N.P.A.
654695	449	1999	BRITISH COLLECTOR'S SET OF 5 BEARS 6-¼in (16cm) each Limited 1,847, white tag, blond, brown-tipped, gold, rose, burgandy mohair, in a wooden box.	N.P.A.
665455	479	1999	BUGS BUNNY (WARNER BROS.) 6in (15cm). Limited 2,500, white tag, holding a hand blown Christopher Radko glass ornament, made for the Warners Bros. Co., U.S.A. only.	N.P.A.
670176	423	1999	CELEBRATION BEAR AND BOOK "TEDDYBAR MIT KNOPF IM OHR" 8-½in (22cm). Limited to 4,000 total (1,000 German and 3,000 English), white tag, blond bear.	N.P.A.
665905	465	1999	CHERISHED TEDDY ENESCO'S DAISY 13in (33cm) Limited 5,000, white tag, large hat, Cherished Teddy on paw.	$295.00
037030	508	1999	CLASSIC BADGER Limited 4,000, white tag, blue coat gold vest, white shirt and light blue tie.	$325.00
067047	508	1999	CLASSIC RATTY Limited 4,000, white tag, white outfit with red and white scarf.	$260.00
000515		1999	CLASSIC 1909 BRASS BEAR 13-¾in (43cm). Yellow tag.	$170.00
006401	427	1999	CLASSIC 1913 DOLLY BEAR 8-½in (22cm). Yellow tag, white head and violet body.	$160.00
006432	427	1999	CLASSIC 1927 PETSY BEAR 8-½in (22cm). Yellow tag, brass mohair.	$160.00
001604	427	1999	CLASSIC 1905 RICHARD BEAR 13-¾in (43cm). Yellow tag, white mohair.	$160.00
001666	427	1999	CLASSIC 1905 RICHARD BEAR 13-¾in (43cm). Yellow tag, gray mohair.	$160.00
001727	427	1999	CLASSIC 1905 RICHARD BEAR 13-¾in (43cm). Yellow tag, beige mohair.	$160.00
001789	427	1999	CLASSIC 1905 RICHARD BEAR 13-¾in (43cm). Yellow tag, caramel mohair.	$160.00
006425	427	1999	CLASSIC 1929 TEDDY BABY 8-½in (22cm). Yellow tag, blue mohair and paw pads.	$180.00
006418	427	1999	CLASSIC 1929 TEDDY BABY 8-½in (22cm). Yellow tag, brown tipped like Happy Bear.	$170.00

Item Ear tag# EAN #	Sortiment Book Vol#1	Vol#2	Year	Description	Value
670336		433	1999	COKE POLAR BEAR 15-¾in (40cm). Limited 1,000, white tag, boxed.	$375.00
665202		474	1999	COLLECTORS UNITED BEAR 8-½in (22cm) Limited 400, pink mohair with a Arabian hat, veil and necklace.	N.P.A.
665844		464	1999	DEW DROP ROSE BEAR 11-¾in (30cm). Limited 3,500, white tag, U.S.A. only.	$325.00
651472		433	1999	DISNEY STEAMBOAT WILLIE 14in (36cm). Limited 10,000, white tag.	$375.00
651489		423	1999	DISNEY WINNIE THE POOH 11in (28cm). Limited 10,000, white tag, wearing a red vest.	$250.00
651434		478	1999 1999 1999	DISNEY WORLD 12TH CONVENTION DAWN BEAR 12-½in (32cm). Limited 1,500. 23-½ (60cm). Limited 25. 31-½in (80cm). Limited 5. White tag, white mohair, ceramic medallion made for Disney World Epcot Center, U.S.A. only.	$350.00 $3500.00 $6500.00
670428		444	1999	EURO. LITTLE SNOWMAN BEAR 4-½in (12cm) Limited 5,000, white tag. Snowman bear with a cooking pot for a hat, holding a small tree.	$145.00
____		474	1999	F.A.O. SCHWARZ ANGEL BEAR 10in (25cm) Limited 2,000, white tag, pink mohair with feather wings and flower headdress, U.S.A. only.	N.P.A.
665936		464	1999	GOOD BEARS "GULLIVER" 15-¾in (40cm). Limited 5,000, white tag, U.S.A. only.	$325.00
028403 028410 670367		422 422 423	1999 1999 1999	GOODBYE DM BEAR 11in (28cm) HELLO EURO BEAR 11in (28cm) HELLO GOODBYE SET 8-¾in (23cm) each. Worldwide edition, white tag, open to end of the year 2000, total 8,890 made, one blue and one apricot tipped fur bears.	$190.00 $190.00 $450.00
652868		451	1999	HAMLEY'S JEREMY BEAR 11in (28cm) Limited 1,500, white tag, reddish brown long mohair, U.K. only.	N.P.A.
660078		455	1999	HOLLAND 4TH BOER (FARMER) BEAR 11-3/4in (30cm) Limited 1,847, white tag, boxed, certificate, blue mohair and wooden shoe design on a scarf.	$350.00
665851		464	1999	HUCK FINN BEAR 11-½in (28m). Limited 1,500, white tag, U.S.A. only.	$275.00
665943	N/A		1999	JACK NICHOLAS BEAR 15-¾in (40cm). Limited 5,000, white tag, U.S.A. only.	$398.00
408533		422	1999	JACKIE BEAR STUDIO 29-½in (75cm). Limited 1,000, white tag.	$1,800.00
658075		456	1999	LAFAYETTEE 5TH BEAR 13in (34cm). Limited 1,500, white tag, dark blue with vest, France only.	N.P.A.
____	N/A		1999	LITTLE MASTRO AND HUMMEL SET 6-1/2in (17cm) and 5-1/2in (14cm) Limited 20,000, white tag.	$350.00
402166	N/A		1999	LULAC RABBIT 1952 REPLICA 17in (43cm). Limited 1,500, white tag.	$240.00
670084	N/A		1999	MARGARET STEIFF MUSEUM BEAR 11-¾in (30cm). Limited, white tag, porcelain medallion, made for the 1999 visitors of the Steiff Museum.	$180.00
670374		423	1999	MILLENNIUM BEAR 17in (43cm) Worldwide edition open until the year end 2000, white tag.	$360.00
651649		478	1999	MINNIE MOUSE CHRISTMAS ORNAMENT 6in (15cm) Limited 1,928, for the Walt Disney Co., U.S.A. only.	N.P.A.
400933	N/A		1999	MONK KING 7-¼in (19cm). Limited 1,200, white tag.	$400.00
998744	N/A		1999	MORTIZ POSTMAN BEAR 14in (36cm). Limited 2,000, white tag, dressed in a yellow and blue jacket.	$400.00
666025	N/A		1999	NOEL BEAR 15-½in (40cm). Limited 1,500, white tag, wearing a dove necklace.	$250.00

Item Ear tag# EAN #	Sortiment Book Vol#1 Vol#2	Year	Description	Value
665820	479	1999	MICHIGAN J. FROG WARNER BROS. #3 11-¾in (30cm) Limited 2,500, white tag, green, black top hat.	N.P.A.
000379	489	1999	RALPH LAUREN HIGHLAND FLING GOLF BEAR Limited 500, yellow tag, pants, sweater, jacket and hat.	$1,000.00
655487	444	1999	ROSEY TEDDY BABY 11-¼in (29cm) Limited 3,000, white tag, Teddy Baby, vivid pink mohair, Germany only.	$550.00
653113	442	1999	RUMTREIBEAR 10-½in (27cm). Limited 1,500, white tag, rust/brown mohair, dressed like a tramp, made for Idee & Spiel stores.	N.P.A.
665967	N/A	1999	SAN DIEGO ZOO PANDA 12in (32cm). Limited 1,500, white tag, a portion is donated to the Zoo's Center for Reproduction of Endangered Species, U.S.A. only.	$375.00
665981	464	1999	PEACE BEAR 11-½in (28cm). Limited 3000, white tag, wearing a dove medallion necklace.	$198.00
665998	N/A 464	1999	SPLASH BEAR 7in (18cm). Limited 4,000, white tag. Bear stands in a lampost vignette, U.S.A. only.	$160.00
420160	N/A	1999/00	STEIFF CLUB MOURNING BEAR 1912 Limited 9,000, club members only, white tag, with a $50.00 yearly fee.	$350.00
_____	N/A	1999/00	STEIFF CLUB POLAR BEAR ON WHEELS 1910 Limited to club members, white tag, with a $50.00 yearly fee.	$350.00
_____	N/A	1999/00	STEIFF CLUB YEAR 2000 BEAR Limited to club members. Limited 9,450, white tag, club members only, one paw is 1999 the other 2000 in red, creamic medallion.	N.P.A.
407161	421	1999	TEDDY BU 1925 BLOND 11-¾in (30cm). Limited 4,000, white tag, blond mohair with rust vest.	$280.00
407185	422	1999	TEDDY BU 1925 BROWN 11-¾in (30cm). Limited 4,000, white tag, brown mohair with red vest.	$280.00
407178	422	1999	TEDDY BU 1925 WHITE 11-¾in (30cm). Limited 1,500, white tag, white mohair with brown vest.	$280.00
407260	422	1999	TEDDY CLOWN 1926 ROSE 13in (33cm). Limited 5,000, white tag.	$375.00
670114	423	1999	TEDDYBEAR FISHERMAN 13-½in (35cm) Limited 2,000, white tag, dressed in a navy blue fisherman's suit and hat.	N.P.A.
670251	423	1999	TEDDY BEAR TOWN SOLDIER 13-¾in (35cm). Limited 2,000, white tag.	$370.00
030796	422	1999	TEDDY LUCKY CHIMNEY SWEEP 4in (10cm) Limited to production date 12/31/99, white tag, black jacket with HAPPY 2000 on the back.	$120.00
651120	423	1999	TEDDY BEAR PILOT 10-½in (27cm). Limited 1,500, white tag, white mohair, dressed in a blue coat, pants and hat with gold braid.	$450.00
655416	423	1999	TEDDY BEAR RINGMASTER 12-½in (30cm) Limited 1,500, white tag, gold mohair, dressed in a red coat trimmed with gold braid.	$550.00
675249	424	1999	TEDDY PEACE 25-½in (65cm) Limited 1,500, white tag, replica 1925 bear sold at 1st Steiff Festival for DM 189,550.00	N.P.A.
665974	465	1999	UFDC TEDDY 13-½in (35cm) Limited 1,500, white tag, blond, made for the UFDC National Convention, U.S.A. only.	$225.00
993644	N/A	1999	UNICEF BEAR (MOHAIR) Limited edition, white tag, light gold mohair wearing a ceramic disk, with embroidered paw Dasneue Berlin and Haptsladt Fur Kinder made for the children.	N.P.A.
996337	N/A	1999	UNICEF BEAR (PLUSH) 10-¼in (26cm). Blue gray plush.	$125.00

2000

Item		Year	Description	Value
675362		2000	BACCARAT BEAR 10-½in (27cm) Limited 1,000, red mohair, made for the Baccarat company, includes 2 crystal glasses in a gift box & certificate, "Steiff & Baccarat" printed on white ribbon around it's neck.	N.P.A.
655562		2000	BADEN-BADEN BATHING BEAR Limited 3,000, white tag, caramel mohair, shoebutton eyes, wears a 1920's stripped bathing suit, made for the first Steiff festival held in Baden-Baden.	$200.00